Muzzey Junior High Library
Lexington, Massachusetts

EXPERIMENTS WITH STATIC ELECTRICITY

BOOKS BY HARRY SOOTIN

Experiments with Machines and Matter

Experiments with Heat

Experiments with Magnetism and Electricity

Light Experiments for Home Workshop and School Laboratory

Science Experiments with Sound

The Young Experimenter's Workbook (with Laura Sootin)

The Long Search

Experiments with Magnetism

Experiments with Static Electricity

Experiments with Electric Currents

EXPERIMENTS
with static electricity

---

by HARRY SOOTIN

Illustrated by Julio Granda

W · W · NORTON & COMPANY · INC ·
New York

Text Copyright © 1969, 1962 by Harry Sootin
Illustrations Copyright © 1969 by W. W. Norton & Company, Inc.
Library of Congress Catalog Card No. 68-23219
All Rights Reserved
Published simultaneously in Canada by
George J. McLeod Limited, Toronto
Printed in the United States of America
1 2 3 4 5 6 7 8 9 0

CONTENTS

FOREWORD

One of the oldest known facts about electricity is that certain substances, when rubbed, will attract small pieces of paper, cork, pith, and straw. As early as 600 B.C., the Greek philosopher Thales of Miletus is said to have considered this phenomenon carefully. In the case of amber, he attributed such attraction to some living principle, or soul, stirred to action by friction.

Today we call this phenomenon electrostatic attraction. A reasonable explanation for the phenomenon was not found until the twentieth century. What is remarkable is not only that it took twenty-six centuries to explain electrostatic attraction, but also the nature of the modern explanation. How could anyone have foreseen that an understanding of why a bit of paper moves towards an electrified body would involve such modern ideas as the electrical nature of matter, the nuclear model of the atom, and fundamental atomic particles such as the electron and the proton?

It is interesting to note that in 1749, Benjamin Franklin expressed a strong belief that electricity, itself, consisted of minute, mobile particles. However, there was no supporting experimental evidence for this hypothesis until 1897, when J. J. Thomson proved that electrons — the name given to light, mobile, negatively charged atomic particles — are constituents of all matter.

Static electricity lends itself to home experimenting. No elaborate setups are needed; the materials required are either household items, or they are widely available at low cost. Substitutions are usually possible, such as hard rubber for sealing wax, the bottom of a glass jar for a glass rod, and flannel for fur. However, as we shall point out frequently, the weather factor is extremely important. You should conduct these experiments on a *dry* day, for in humid weather the charges produced on rubber or glass may disappear quickly.

There are twenty sets of experiments in this book. Each set is introduced by two pages of text in which fundamental ideas pertaining to the experiments are discussed. The emphasis of the book is on understanding basic principles rather than on arranging complicated experiments.

At the end of this book, under "Further Reading," the reader will find a few useful suggestions on how to go on to a deeper understanding of the topics presented here. Electrostatics is an intrinsically interesting field, and how far the reader progresses depends entirely upon his intellectual curiosity and energy.

Note that these abbreviations and symbols are used throughout this book:

North-pole = N-pole
South-pole = S-pole
volts = v
amperes = amp
one inch = 1″
one foot = 1′
number six dry cell = #6 dry cell
resistance = R

north to south N–S
plus (positive) +
minus (negative) —
dry cell 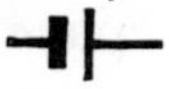
switch 
bulb (lamp) 
resistance 
fuse

WHAT YOU SHOULD KNOW

...about making a pith-ball electroscope

To prepare for your experiments with static electricity, you are going to suspend a piece of light material (pith) by a silk thread. The thread will be tied to a bent wire so that the pith ball may swing freely.

The suspended pith ball can be used as an *electroscope*, which is an instrument for detecting the presence of an electric charge on any object.

Static electricity, the subject we shall be concerned with in this section, was discovered early in history. About 600 B.C., Thales, a Greek philosopher, observed that amber, after being rubbed between the fingers, attracted light objects like threads and bits of straw.

It was William Gilbert (1540-1600), an English investigator of magnetism, who noted about 2,200 years after Thales that *many* substances have the same property as amber, that is, they attract light substances after being rubbed.

Gilbert gave the name *electrics* to such substances. The Greek word for amber is *elektron.*

How can one tell whether or not an object has acquired an electric charge by friction or rubbing? The object looks the same after rubbing as it did before. One way is to bring the object near lightweight bodies like bits of paper, straw, etc. If these light bodies are *attracted*, then the object has an electric charge.

But instead of testing with bits of thread or paper, a suspended pith ball is more convenient. For example, a hard-rubber comb rubbed on wool attracts a neutral pith ball just as it attracts bits of thread or paper.

Other experimental advantages of the pith-ball electroscope are these:

The movement of a pith ball is easy to see.

The pith ball may swing toward or away from an electrified object without touching nearby materials like wood, wire, etc.

The pith ball, if it should acquire a charge, will retain it for some time — if the surrounding air is dry.

Note about the experiments which follow:

Your results will be better if you perform the static electricity experiments on a *dry day*. Be sure you use a *dry* silk thread or the electric charge may leak off the pith ball.

WHAT TO DO

...making a pith ball electroscope

1. Diagram of a pith ball electroscope.

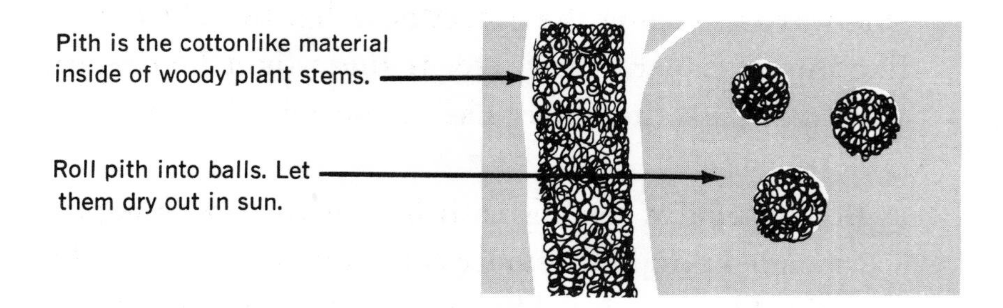

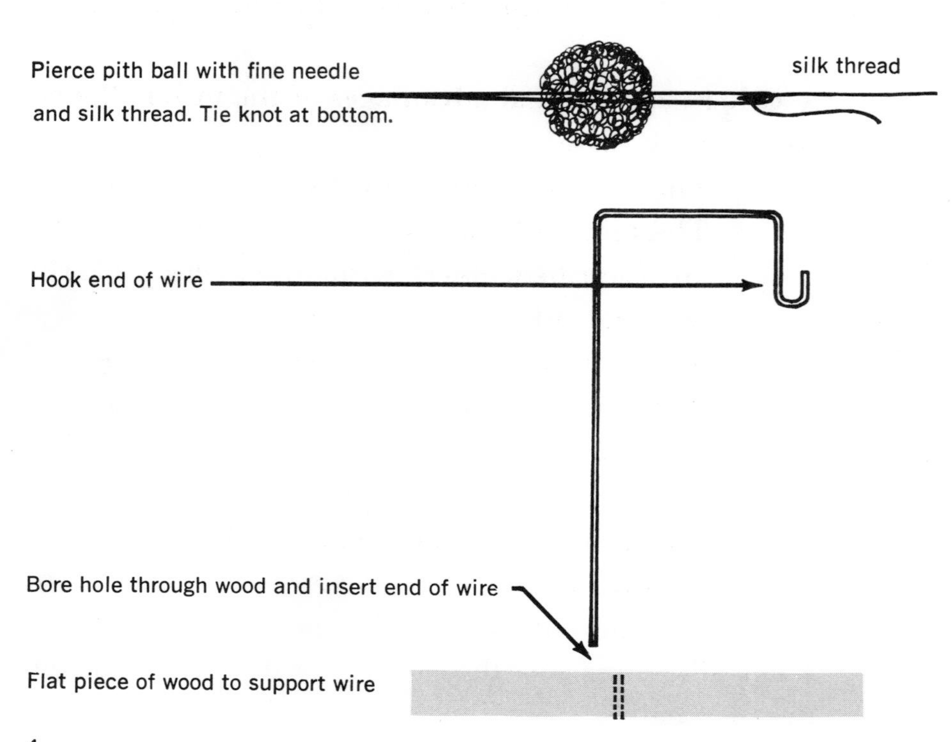

2. What you need and how to put the parts together.

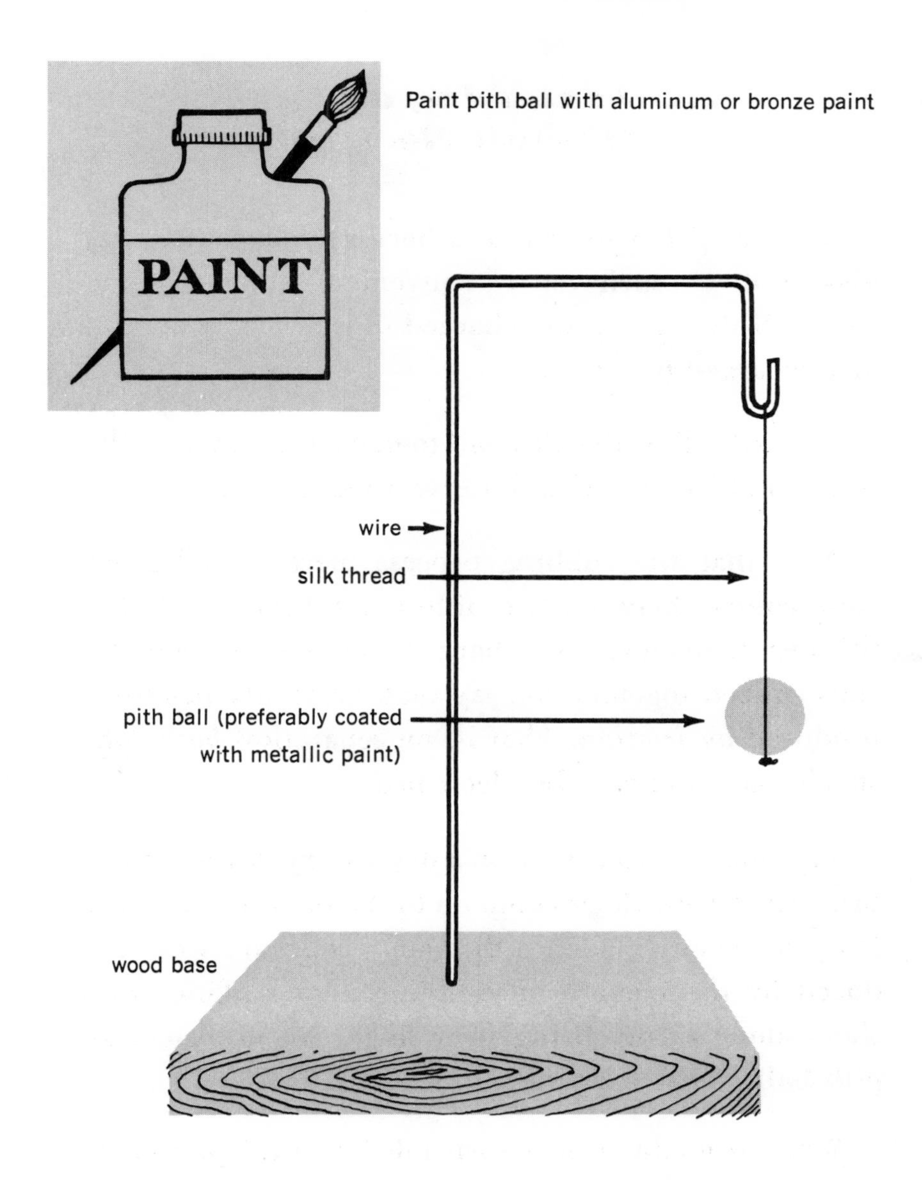

WHAT YOU SHOULD KNOW

...about using a pith-ball electroscope

You are going to charge a hard-rubber comb, or a glass rod — whichever is convenient — by friction. You will then bring the charged object near a neutral or uncharged pith ball.

You will allow the pith ball to make contact with the charged object and then observe what happens.

Note that the rubbing process merely establishes close contact between two different substances. When this results in an electric charge being left on the materials rubbed together, we say that electricity has been produced by *friction*. That is, on separation *both* substances are found to be electrified.

Try combing your hair on a dry wintry day and then bring the hard-rubber comb up to the neutral pith ball. Do you see any evidence that any electricity was produced by the friction or rubbing? Try scuffing your shoes along a rug. Bring your finger up to a neutral pith ball. What happens?

When brought near a suspended neutral pith ball,

every electrified object will cause the following three reactions on the part of the pith ball: *attraction, contact, repulsion.* In other words, you will see the pith ball move toward the electrified object, touch it, and then immediately fly away from it as if repelled by some force.

The experiments of Gilbert served to remove much of the mystery from *electrostatic attraction*, which is the modern term for the attraction between electrified objects and light bodies. For one thing, he showed that the properties of a lodestone and electrified amber were *different.*

Curiously enough, Gilbert was unaware of, or paid little attention to, the *repulsion* between charged bodies. Apparently he regarded *attraction* as the *important property* of electrified objects.

When a charged pith ball is touched with the finger, a connection is made between the pith ball and the earth. Electric charges then flow *into* or *out of* the pith ball until a neutral state is reached. We call this process *grounding* the pith ball. As a result, the pith ball returns to the neutral condition it was in at first, that is, before an electrified object touched it.

Tip about the experiments which follow:
On a damp day, the electric charges produced by friction may leak off before you can test for them. Do *all* your static electricity experiments on a *dry* day.

WHAT TO DO

...now that you have made a simple electroscope, practice using it

1. Rub a glass rod with silk. If you can't get a glass rod, then substitute a hard-rubber comb rubbed with fur or flannel.

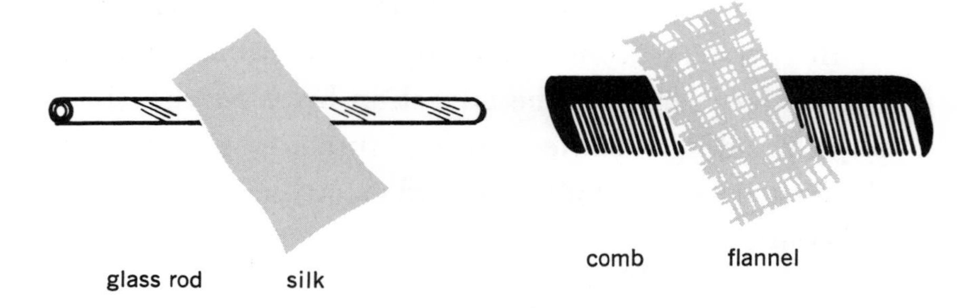

2. Now bring the rubbed object up to an uncharged pith ball.

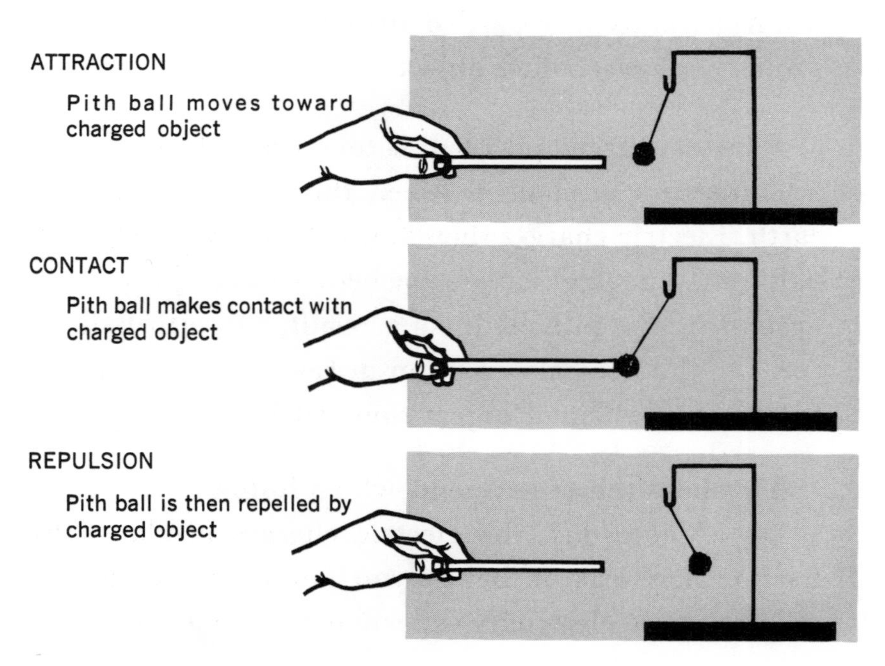

3. Before using electroscope to test a **different** body or object, remember to touch the pith ball with your finger. This "grounds" the pith ball, thus freeing it from its charge.

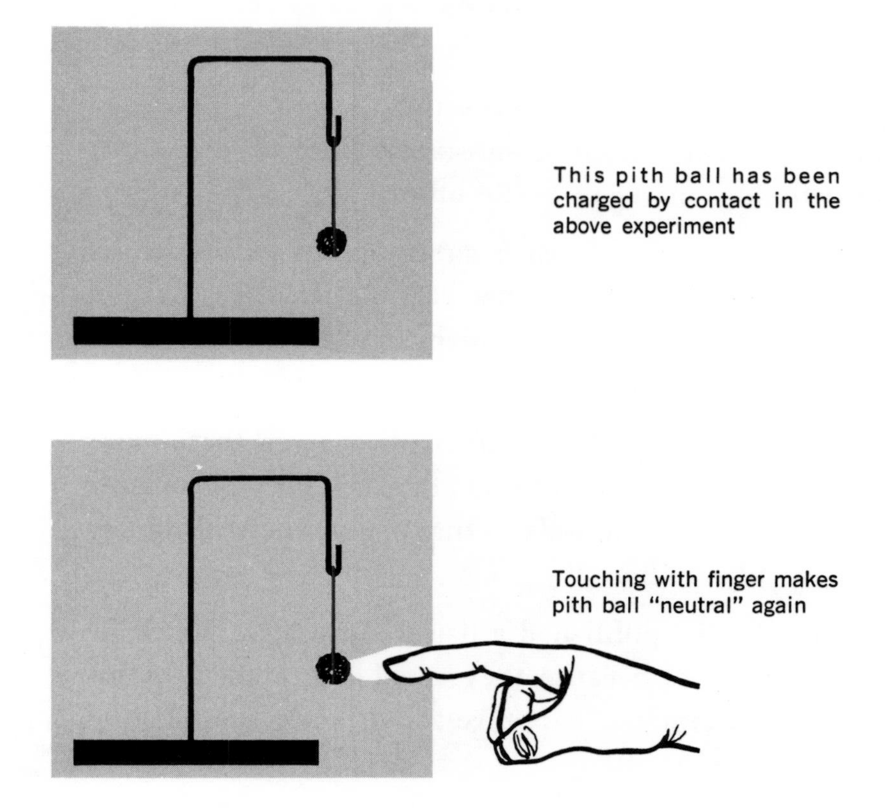

This pith ball has been charged by contact in the above experiment

Touching with finger makes pith ball "neutral" again

4. Use your electroscope to test the silk or fur or flannel for an electric charge. Do this **both** before and after rubbing the above substances. Do you detect a charge on the silk or fur or flannel?

WHAT YOU SHOULD KNOW

...about electrifying different substances by friction

In the next section of experiments, you are going to bring pairs of different substances into close contact by rubbing one against the other.

You can then test *each* substance in each pair by means of your pith-ball electroscope. In this way you will be able to find out which substances acquire an electric charge on rubbing and which do not.

As mentioned before, Gilbert discovered that amber is not the only substance that attracts light objects after being rubbed. He found out that many other substances behave like amber.

In 1600, he published a list of substances which he called *electrics* because they acted like amber. In his list were diamond, sapphire, opal, rock crystal, and others.

Gilbert also compiled a list of substances which, after rubbing, *did not* attract light objects like threads or bits of paper. His list of *non-electrics* included *all the metals*.

About 150 years after Gilbert's investigations, another Englishman, Stephen Gray (1696-1736), finally succeeded in electrifying metal objects. He took care to place the rubbed metal objects on insulators, thus preventing the charge from escaping.

Today we know that practically all bodies or objects may be electrified. Certain materials, however, are more readily electrified than others when rubbed together: for example, sealing wax with fur or flannel; glass with silk; hard rubber with fur or flannel, etc.

Gilbert, who was an excellent experimenter, worked with simple detecting instruments in the foggy atmosphere of London. Leakage of electric charges into the damp air often made his results uncertain.

Otto von Guericke (1602-1686), a German scientist famous for his experiments with pumps and vacuums, was also interested in frictional electricity. He devised one of the earliest electrostatic machines. This was simply a device that reduced the labor involved in rubbing an object in order to produce an electric charge on its surface. He mounted a large sulphur sphere on a shaft through its center to make it easier to rotate the sphere. As the ball of sulphur rotated with the hand held against it, electricity was produced by friction.

Note about the experiments which follow:

Most of the materials used in these experiments are easily obtained. Sealing wax is useful because a good charge can be produced on it by rubbing with fur or wool or flannel. It is inexpensive, and a stick of it may be purchased at any store where office supplies are sold.

WHAT TO DO

...more tests with your pith ball electroscope

1. Try producing an electrical charge on each of the following objects. Bring each rubbed substance up to electroscope as before. Remember to discharge pith ball by touching it with finger **before** testing the next object.

Don't forget this step

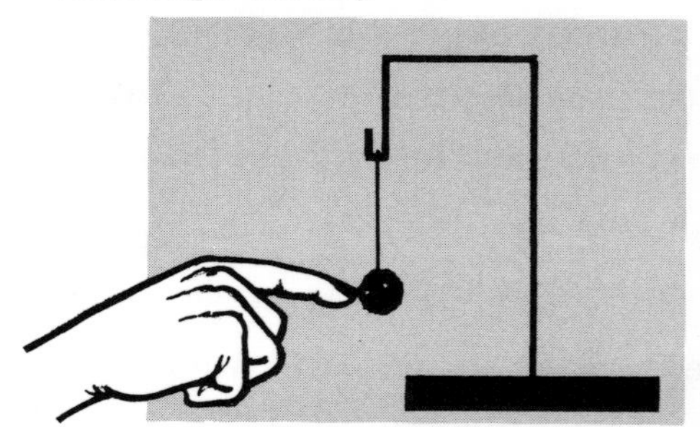

Getting rid of charge on pith ball

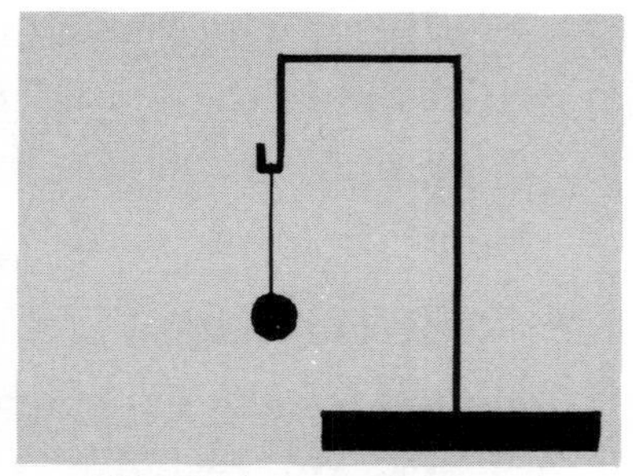

Pith ball is now neutral and ready for use

Common Objects

Hard-Rubber Comb

Rub with fur or wool or flannel.

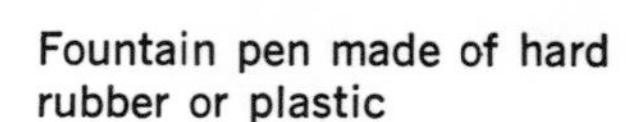

Fountain pen made of hard rubber or plastic

Rub with fur or wool or flannel.

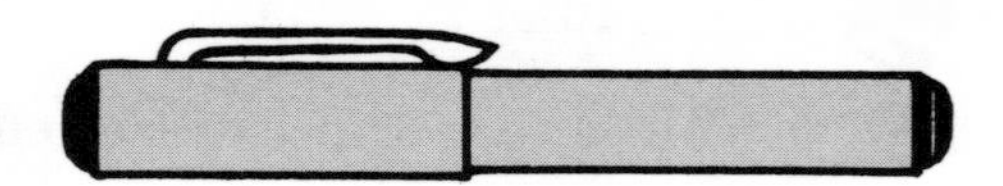

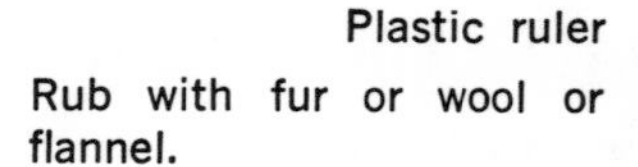

Plastic ruler

Rub with fur or wool or flannel.

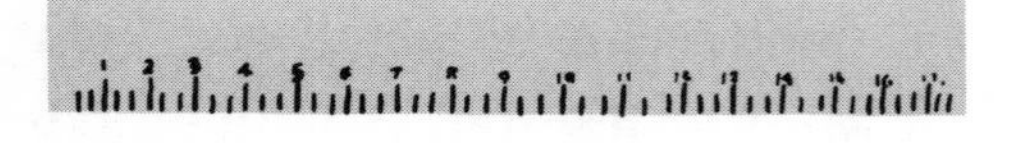

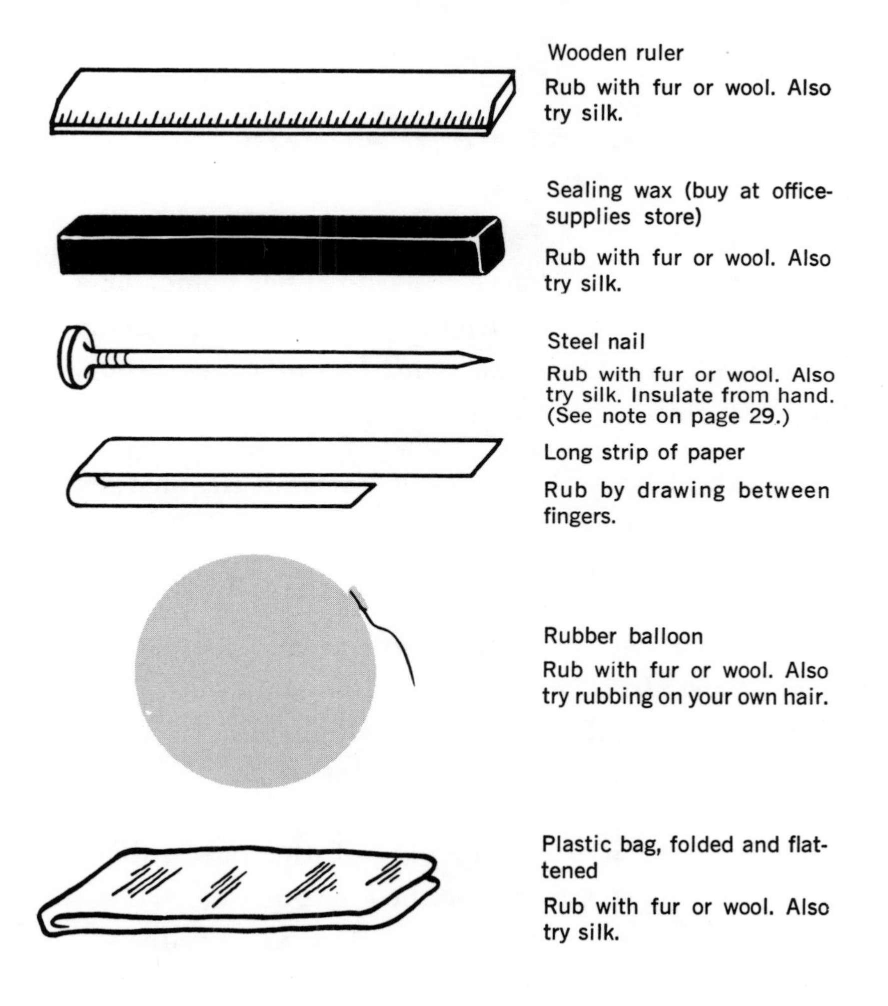

2. NOTE: Try rubbing different objects you may have at hand. If you get a charge with wool or fur, then see if silk will also produce an electric charge on the same object.

WHAT YOU SHOULD KNOW

...about electrostatic attraction

You are going to charge a hard-rubber comb, or a piece of sealing wax, by friction. You will then bring the charged object close to *small bits* of paper, wood, aluminum foil, copper or iron.

You will also try the attractive force of the charged comb or sealing wax on a large, light, suspended object like an *aluminum-foil* pie plate.

Finally, you will try to find out if such a charged object has poles. In other words, will one end of an electrified piece of sealing wax *attract* light objects while the other end *repels* these *same* objects?

Remember that *only the part* of the hard-rubber comb or sealing wax that is rubbed becomes electrified. The electric charges stay where they are produced; namely, at the rubbed end of the comb or sealing wax.

Where your hand touches the comb or sealing wax, *no electric charge* is present. In the first place, the part in contact with the hand was not rubbed; in the second place, even if this part had a charge, contact with the hand would ground that portion of the object and make it neutral.

Notice that substances readily electrified by friction — hard-rubber, sealing wax, glass, silk, amber, wool — are all *insulators*, or non-conductors, of electricity. Charges formed on insulators *do not* move from point to point easily; they more or less stay where they have been produced.

Why can't an iron rod be electrified by friction? It *can* be — *if* the charge is prevented from escaping to nearby materials. In a conductor — that is, any metal — charges formed by friction distribute themselves immediately *all over* the surface of the conductor. Unless well insulated, the metallic object will lose its charge to the earth very quickly.

If one end of a stick of electrified sealing wax attracts bits of paper, will the other end repel them? Try it. Do electrified objects have poles? Will an electrified object attract magnetic as well as non-magnetic substances?

Remember that all light substances or bodies, regardless of what they are made of, are attracted to electrified objects.

To insulate an object electrically, we must place it in contact with a substance through which electric charges can pass only *with difficulty* — if at all. Such a substance is called an *insulator*, or *dielectric*.

WHAT TO DO

. . . *will electrified bodies attract* *all or only some light objects?*

1. Sprinkle tiny bits of different substances on a sheet of paper.

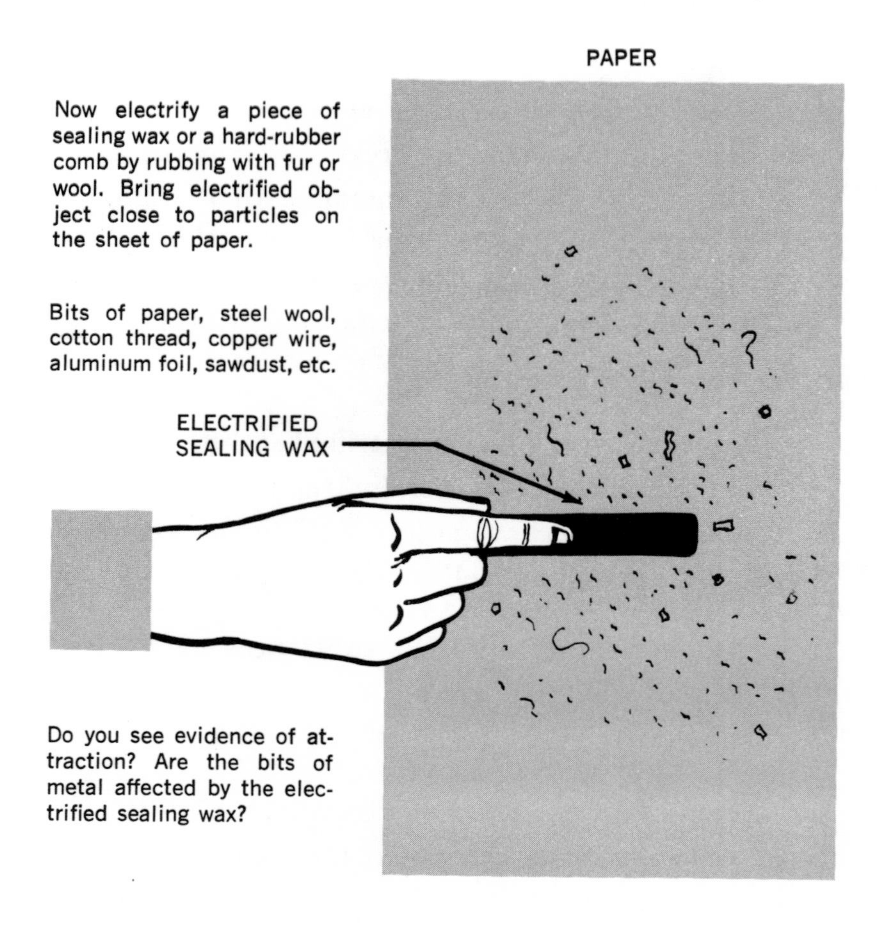

Now electrify a piece of sealing wax or a hard-rubber comb by rubbing with fur or wool. Bring electrified object close to particles on the sheet of paper.

Bits of paper, steel wool, cotton thread, copper wire, aluminum foil, sawdust, etc.

Do you see evidence of attraction? Are the bits of metal affected by the electrified sealing wax?

2. Now see if larger objects will also be attracted to an electrified body. Try this:

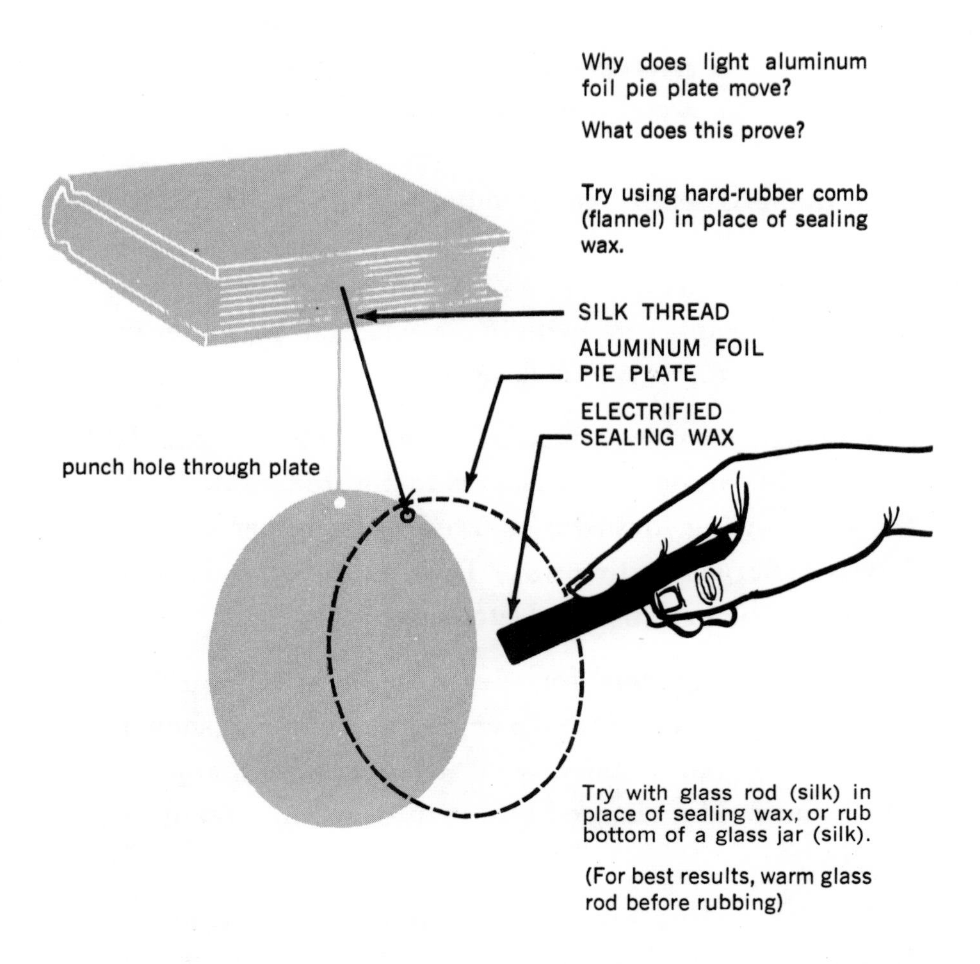

3. Try rubbing the other end of the comb or sealing wax and then repeat the above experiments. Do you observe attraction? Repulsion? Does an electrified object have poles similar to those found in magnets?

WHAT YOU SHOULD KNOW

...about the attraction between large objects and charged bodies

In the next set of experiments, you are going to suspend a wooden yardstick by a silk thread. After balancing the yardstick so that it can move freely in a horizontal plane, try bringing a charged object near each end of the suspended yardstick.

You will also try a similar experiment with a balanced drinking straw as shown in the diagram. Does the straw swing toward a charged hard-rubber comb? Toward charged sealing wax? Do you think a balanced straw may be used as an electroscope? Try it.

You will also test for electrostatic attraction between a charged object and a coping saw blade as shown in the diagram. Finally, you will see what happens when you hold a charged object near a thin stream of water.

A ruler resting on a table will not move when a charged object is brought near it. However, the same ruler suspended from a light silk thread will be drawn toward the electrified body. Why?

William Gilbert used a *pivoted steel needle* mounted

on an insulator in his investigation of *electrics* or things "which attract in the same manner as amber does." (See page 34.)

Gilbert rubbed amber, sapphire, diamond, and other substances, then brought each rubbed substance close to the end of a steel needle that was balanced on a sharp point. If the needle, which could move freely in a horizontal plane, was attracted, Gilbert classified the substance as an *electric*; if not, he listed it as a *nonelectric*.

Later it was discovered that all light objects are attracted to electrified bodies; and heavy objects, if suspended so that they can move readily, are also drawn to electrified bodies.

Solids may also be electrified by liquids; for example, metal pipes are charged by the gasoline flowing through them. For this reason all gasoline pumps are grounded or connected with the earth.

Try holding a sheet of paper against a flat surface like a door panel. Rub the paper briskly with your hand. Does the paper seem to "stick" to the door panel? Why?

In printing plants, friction often causes static charges to accumulate on sheets of paper. As a result, the sheets stick to one another. Adding moisture to the air by means of an air conditioner can prevent this, for moist air allows the charge to leak off the paper. Another remedy is to ground the paper as it passes through the presses.

WHAT TO DO

...attracting other large objects to an electrified body

1. How to make a suspended wooden ruler respond to electrostatic attraction.

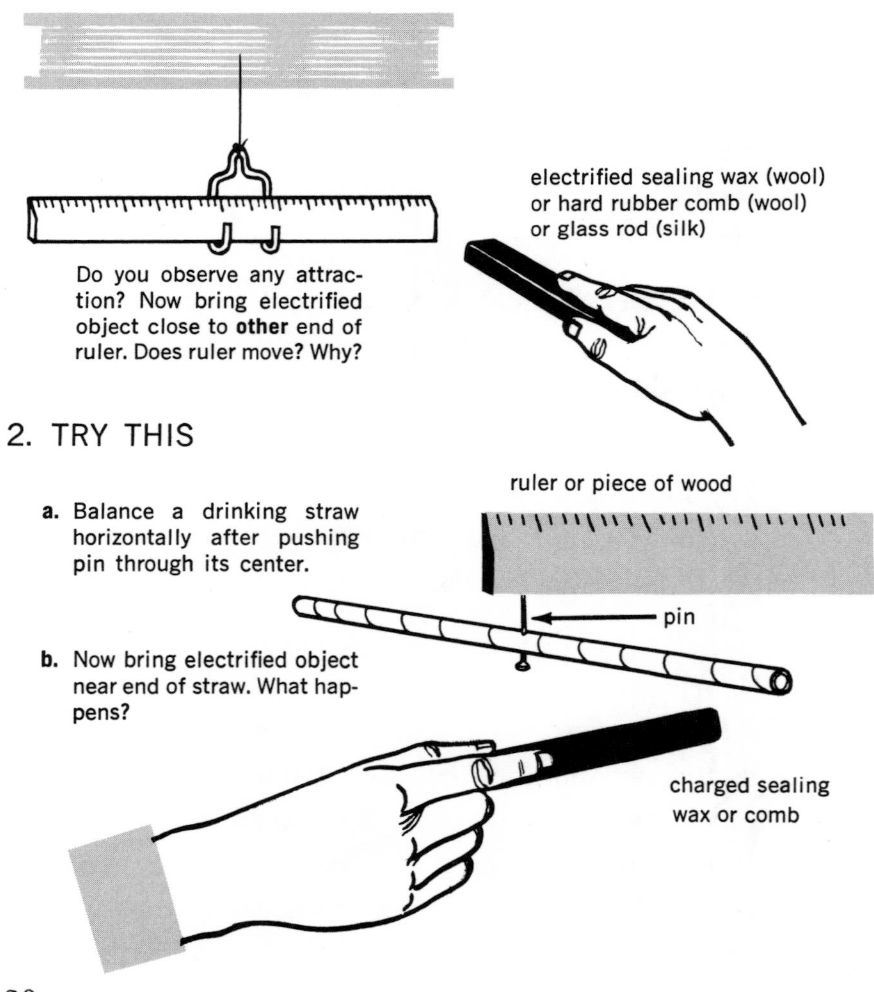

Do you observe any attraction? Now bring electrified object close to **other** end of ruler. Does ruler move? Why?

2. TRY THIS

   a. Balance a drinking straw horizontally after pushing pin through its center.

   b. Now bring electrified object near end of straw. What happens?

3. TRY THIS

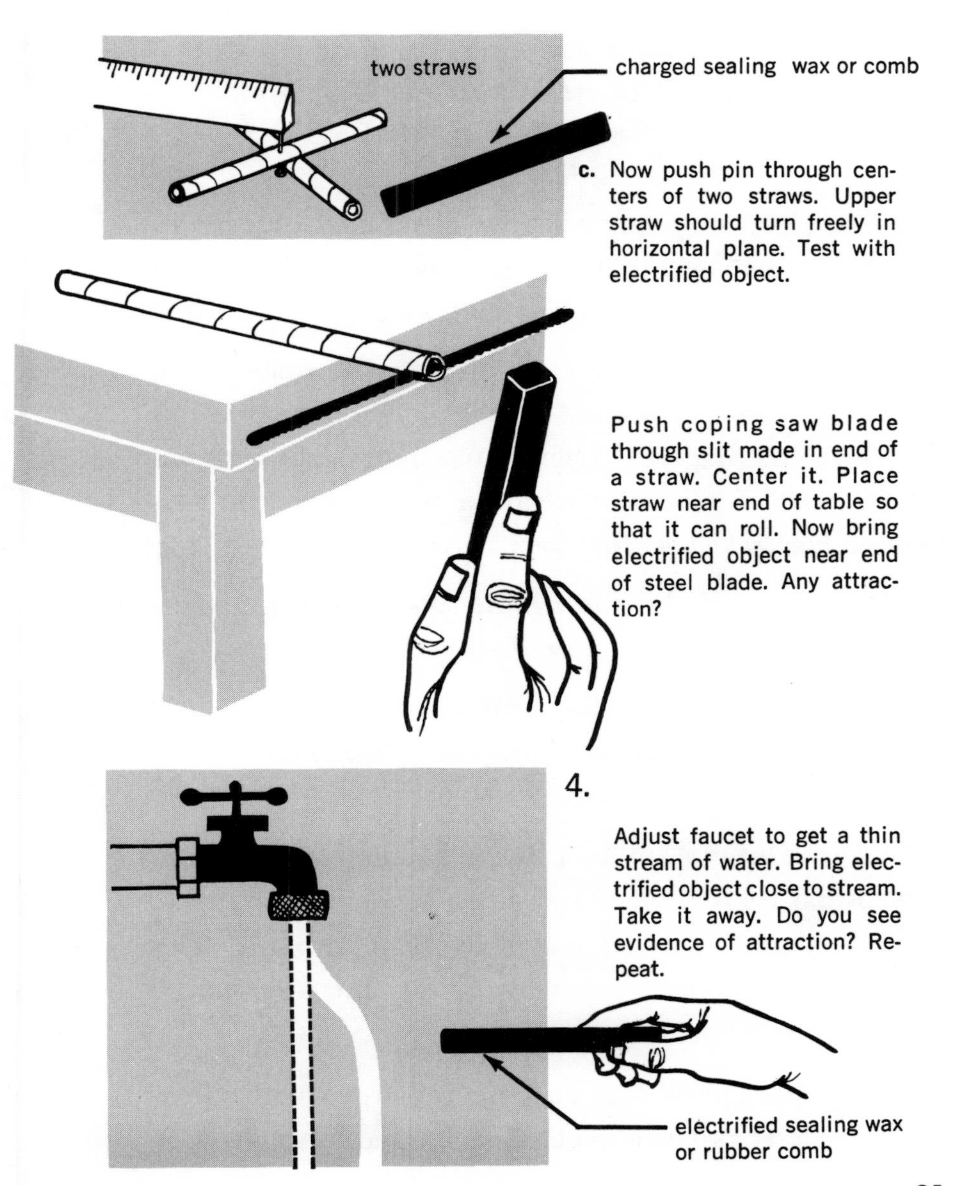

c. Now push pin through centers of two straws. Upper straw should turn freely in horizontal plane. Test with electrified object.

Push coping saw blade through slit made in end of a straw. Center it. Place straw near end of table so that it can roll. Now bring electrified object near end of steel blade. Any attraction?

4.

Adjust faucet to get a thin stream of water. Bring electrified object close to stream. Take it away. Do you see evidence of attraction? Repeat.

WHAT YOU SHOULD KNOW

...*about two different kinds of electricity or electrification*

So far, you have proved that electrified objects attract light bodies. For thousands of years this was all that was known about electrification.

In going on to the next step, you will suspend an electrified piece of sealing wax in a wire "cradle" as shown in the diagram. Then you will try bringing another piece of *electrified* sealing wax up to the suspended *electrified* sealing wax.

Next you will do this again, this time using electrified glass instead of electrified sealing wax.

Finally you will try bringing electrified glass close to the ends of a suspended piece of *electrified* sealing wax.

Charles Dufay (1698-1739), a French scientist, observed that there seemed to be *two kinds* of electricity. He called one *vitreous* and the other *resinous*. The *vitreous* commonly occurs on glass; the *resinous* on hard rubber or sealing wax.

Dufay discovered that an object charged with vitreous electricity *repels* objects also charged with vitreous electricity; that an object charged with *vitreous* electricity *attracts* objects charged with *resinous* electricity.

Soon after Dufay's investigations, Benjamin Franklin (1706-1790) gave the names *positive* (+) and *negative* (−) to the two kinds of electrification discovered by the French scientist.

A *positively* electrified body is one that acts like a glass rod that has been rubbed with silk. A *negatively* electrified body is one that acts like a piece of sealing wax that has been rubbed with flannel.

To find out what *kind* of electrification a body has, we make use of this law: *Like* electric charges *repel*; *unlike* electrical charges *attract*.

Here, too, as in testing iron or steel for magnetism, *repulsion* is the important reaction. Remember that *all* light bodies are attracted to electrified objects. Therefore we must look for *repulsion*, because *if* a substance possesses an electric charge it will be *repelled* by an object with a *similar* electric charge.

As mentioned earlier, men for many centuries were unaware of repulsion between electrified objects — perhaps because they found the *attraction* between light bodies and electrified objects so mystifying.

You might also try suspending a hard-rubber comb or piece of plastic by a silk thread. Now electrify each by rubbing with wool. How would you determine whether the charge on the suspended object is positive or negative? Try it.

WHAT TO DO

...proving that there are two kinds of electrification

1. How do two objects, each made of the **same** material and each rubbed with the same kind of material, act toward each other?

   TRY THIS

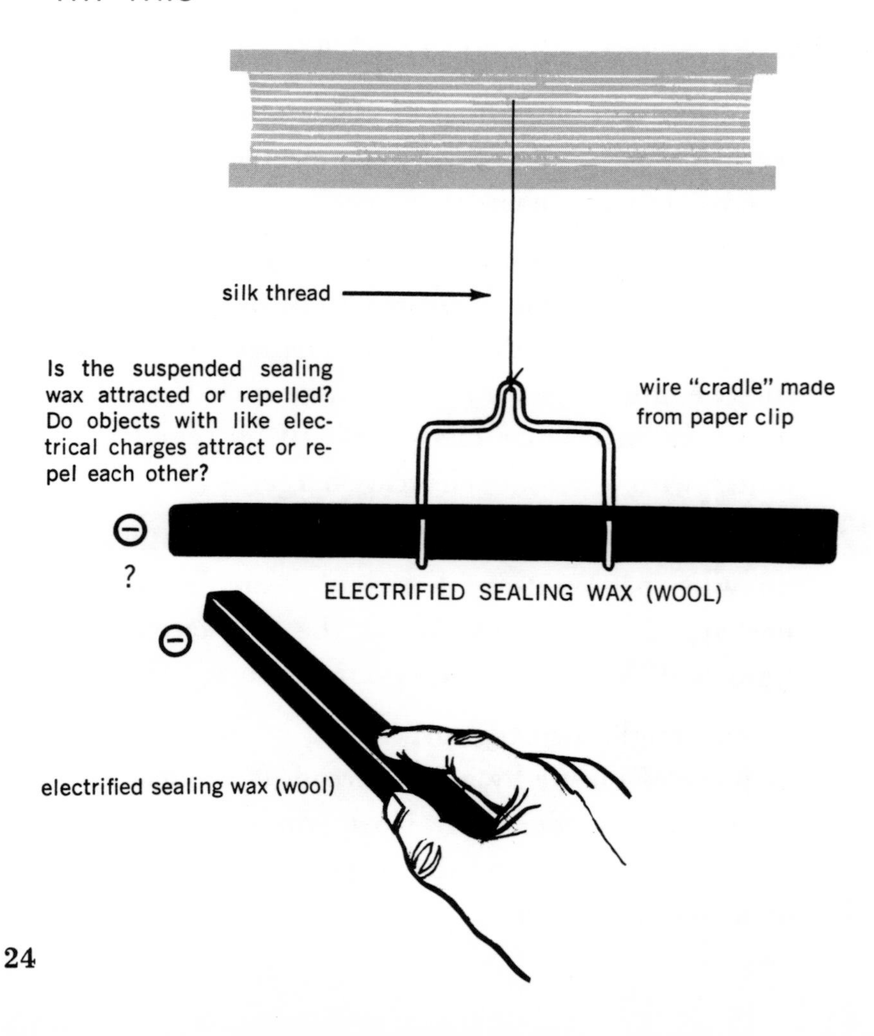

2. Now try this, rub a glass rod with silk. Bring it close to the suspended electrified sealing wax.

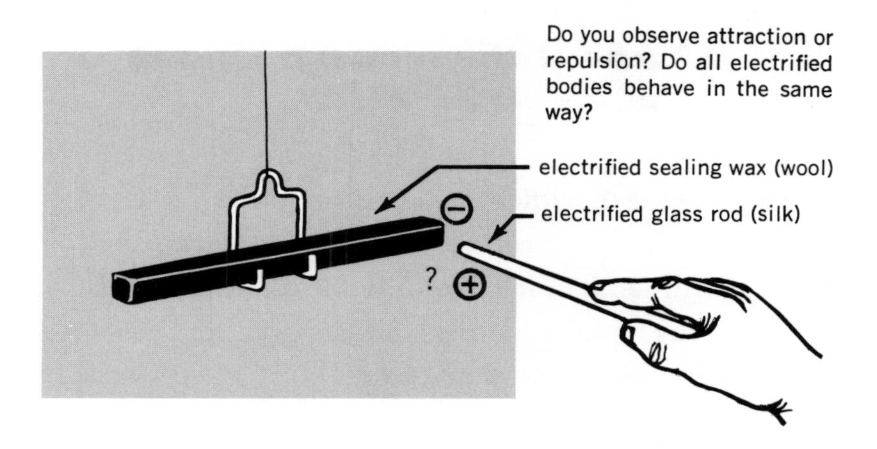

3. How about the reaction between uncharged or neutral sealing wax and charged sealing wax? Try it. Can you explain what happens?

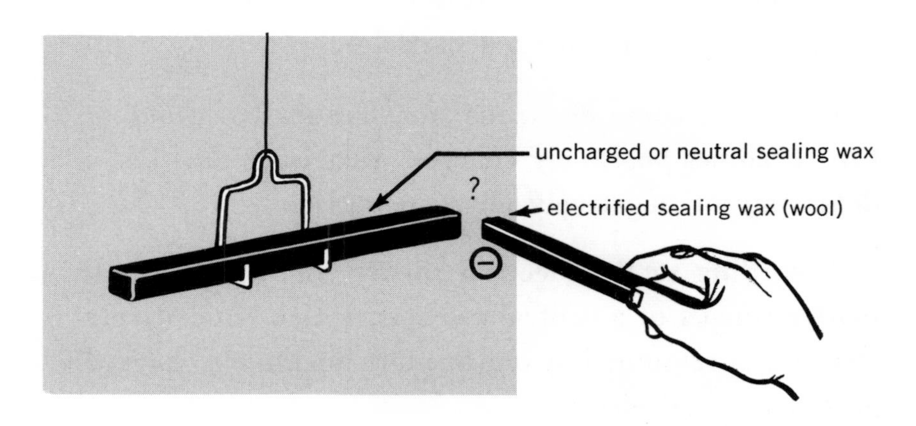

WHAT YOU SHOULD KNOW

. . . about the modern theory of electrification

In the next experiments, you are going to start with *uncharged*, or *neutral*, sealing wax and *uncharged*, or *neutral*, fur or flannel. Neutral means that a substance contains equal quantities of positive and negative electricity, as do most materials.

The rubbing action causes such close contact between sealing wax and flannel that some *negatively* charged particles, called *electrons*, *move* from the flannel to the sealing wax.

By acquiring electrons, the sealing wax becomes *negatively* charged, that is, it now has an excess of electrons or negatively charged particles.

By losing some electrons, the flannel (or wool or fur) becomes *positively* charged, that is, it now has a *deficiency* of negatively charged particles.

According to the electron theory, the atoms in all matter consist of a central *nucleus,* which is positively charged, surrounded by one or more negatively charged particles called electrons.
Under normal conditions the number of electrons located in orbits outside an atom's nucleus is equal to

the number of *protons,* or positively charged particles, in the nucleus. The *neutron,* the other fundamental particle in the atomic nucleus, has *no* charge.

The protons are *within* the nucleus of each atom; the electrons are grouped *around* the nucleus. Electrons are relatively light particles; a proton, however, is about 1,836 times heavier than an electron.

Again, according to the electron theory, the production of an electric charge is explained by the addition or subtraction of *electrons* from materials. In solids, the much heavier protons or positive charges are not easily dislodged from the atom; hence, the positively charged particles are regarded as more or less fixed or immobile in solid substances.

Under normal conditions, each atom of a substance is *neutral.* However, when two *different* substances are placed in close contact, one of them usually attracts electrons from the other. Both substances then cease to be electrically neutral.

Keep in mind that an *excess* of electrons causes an object to be *negatively* charged. A *deficiency* of electrons causes an object to be *positively* charged. The charge on any electrified substance is the result of a *gain* or *loss* of electrons by the substance.

Note about the experiments which follow:
Try a hard-rubber comb and flannel in place of the sealing wax and flannel.

WHAT TO DO

. . . understanding why objects acquire an electric charge

1. Before rubbing your sealing wax with fur or wool, bring each object up to a neutral pith ball.

Why is there no attraction or repulsion?

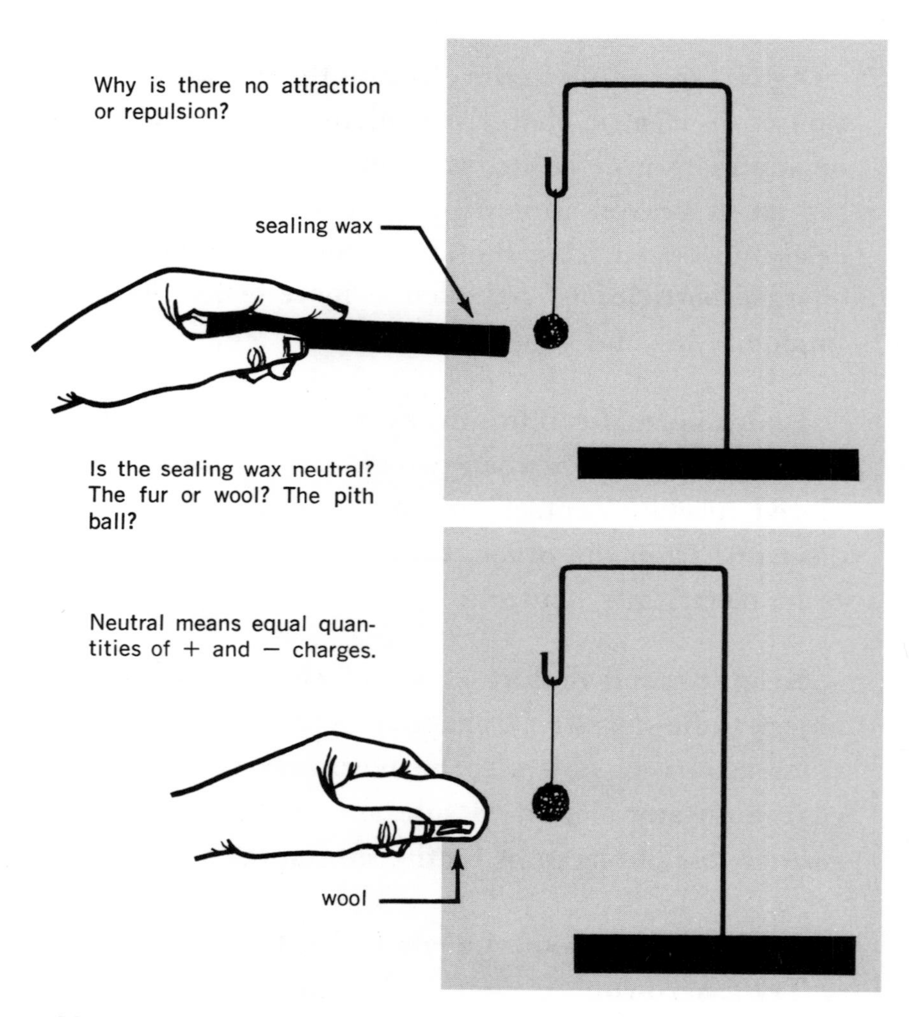

Is the sealing wax neutral? The fur or wool? The pith ball?

Neutral means equal quantities of + and − charges.

2. Try to rub some electrons or negative particles of electricity **off** the wool cloth and **on** to your sealing wax.

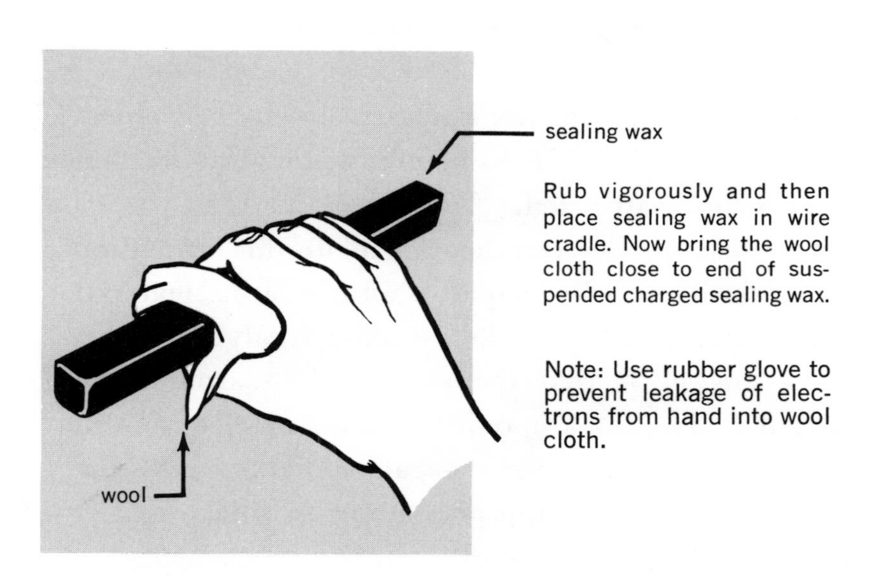

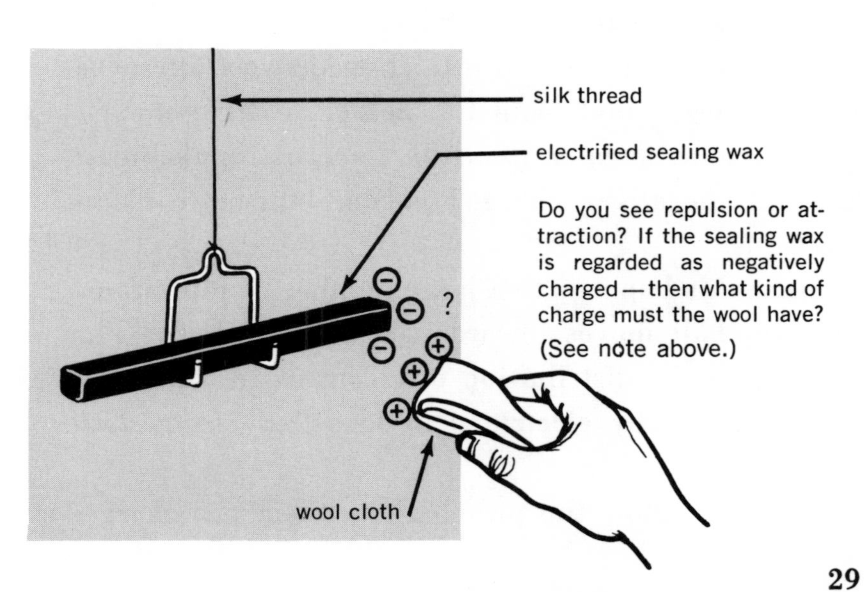

WHAT YOU SHOULD KNOW

...about charging an object by contact

You are going to bring a negatively charged object near a neutral pith ball. As before, you will notice that the pith ball is attracted.

How does the electron theory explain this attraction, since pith, like cord or paper, is an insulating material through which electrons do *not* move freely?

The answer is that the electric field around the charged body causes a redistribution of electrons in the pith atoms. The nearby negative charge causes the cloud of electrons in the pith atoms to shift slightly, due to repulsion. As a result of this displacement, the center of the electron cloud falls towards the far side of the nucleus. The force of attraction between the negatively charged body and the nearer positive nucleus then becomes greater than the force of repulsion between the negatively charged body and the more distant electrons.

Since this happens to a large number of pith atoms, the pith ball moves towards the charged body. This shifting in the distribution of electrons in a material due to a nearby electric field is called *electrostatic induction.*

You will allow the pith ball to touch the charged

object. Immediately you will observe repulsion. Why repulsion *after* attraction and contact? Electrons move into the pith ball from the negatively charged body at the moment of contact. Now the pith ball has "extra" electrons, making it negative. It swings away because now both pith ball and charged body are negative, and *like charges repel.*

Do you now understand why it helps to coat the pith ball with metallic paint? This coating gives improved results because metals are good conductors of electricity; that is, free electrons move over the metallic surface readily.

Keep this in mind: An object charged by contact always acquires a charge of the *same* sign as the electrified body which *touched* it. Why? Try checking the charge on a pith ball after contact by bringing up an object with an opposite electric charge.

Also note that in solids, the positive charges stay in place, that is, remain within the atomic nuclei. Remember that except when heat makes them vibrate, or move, the positively charged particles, or protons, are regarded as more or less fixed in position.

WHAT TO DO

...*charging a pith ball by contact*

1. Suppose you want to give a pith ball a negative charge. First bring the negatively electrified object close to the pith ball.

The free electrons or (—) charges on the pith-ball coating
are repelled to the far side
Why?

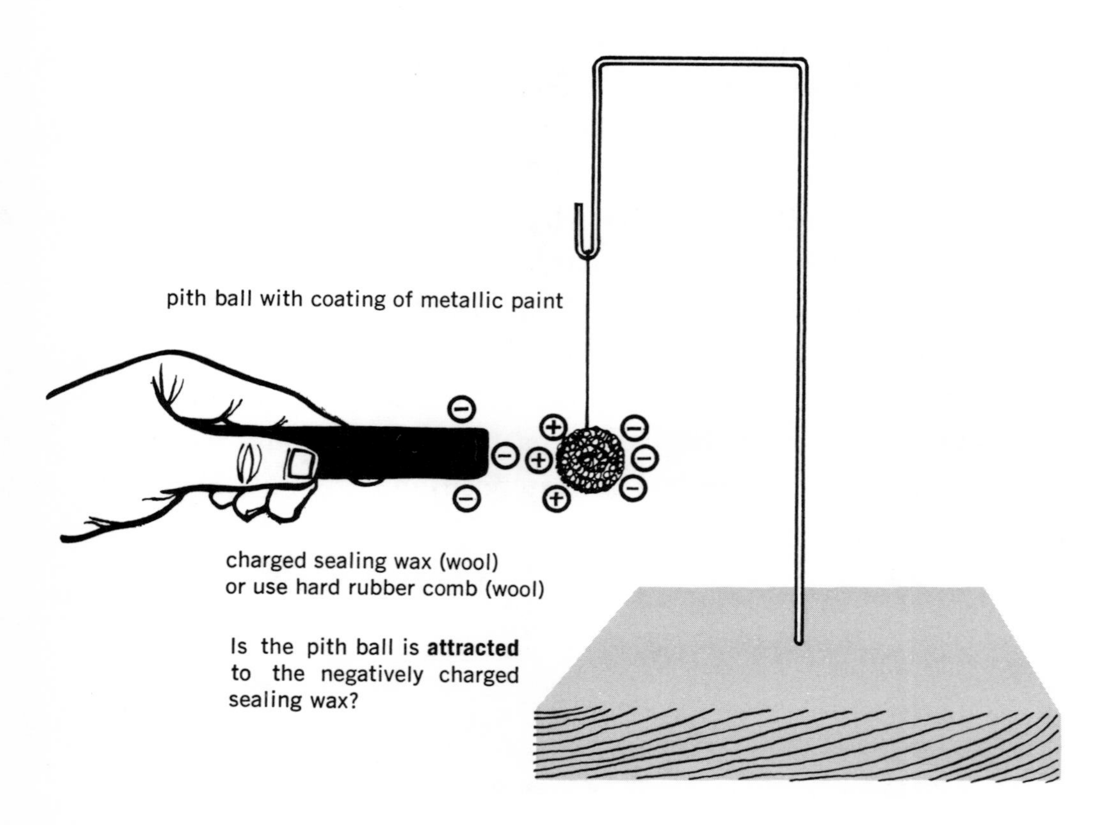

2. Let the pith ball touch the negatively charged sealing wax.

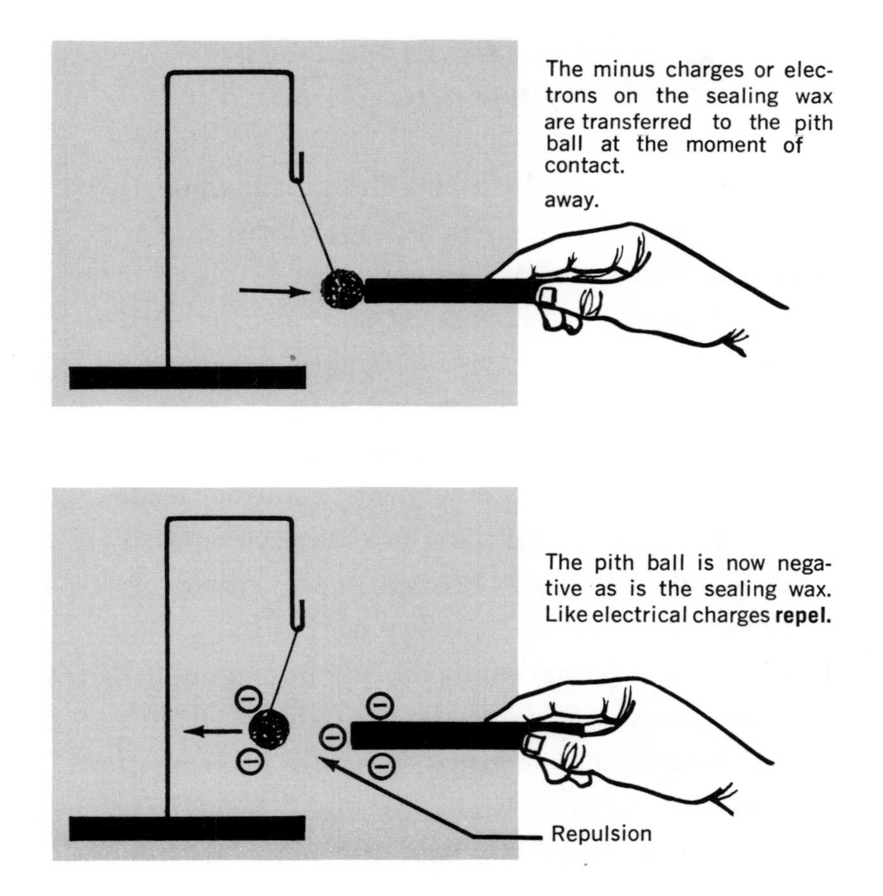

3. Now that you have learned that contact with a **negatively** charged object makes a pith ball **negative,** try charging a pith ball **positively** by using an electrified glass rod (silk). **Before** proceeding remember to make your pith ball neutral again by touching or grounding it.

WHAT YOU SHOULD KNOW

...about the metal-leaf electroscope

You are going to make a leaf electroscope and then enclose it in either a glass jar or a metal case.

An electroscope is an instrument that will detect the presence of an electric charge. It may also be used to distinguish between positive and negative charges, and to compare the amounts of electric charge.

The earliest form of electroscope, as mentioned on page 19, was Gilbert's *versorium* or "rotating needle." He mounted a light metallic arrow on a pivot. When an electrified substance was brought near either of its ends, the arrow was attracted. Try it.

The modern explanation of this phenomenon, called *electrostatic induction* (see page 30), is based on our understanding of the electrical structure of all matter. Let us say that a negatively charged rod is brought near the arrow point. Electrons near the point are immediately repelled toward the opposite end of the arrow. A net positive charge is thus produced at the point and a net negative charge at the more distant end of the arrow. The result is that the positively charged point is attracted to the negatively charged rod.

Later, other electroscopes were devised. Among the

most common were the following: two pith balls suspended from fine silver wires, double straws, and a pair of linen threads. Each of these devices was based on the principle of the repulsion between two similarly charged bodies.

In 1787, Abraham Bennet, English scientist, invented the modern form of gold-leaf electroscope. You will use light aluminum foil instead of gold leaf, and a jar or a can in place of the glass lampshade employed by Bennet.

Actually, a thick copper wire with two aluminum leaves attached to one end may be used as an electroscope, provided that you suspend the wire from a silk thread. The purpose of a case or container is (a) to prevent the disturbance of the delicate leaves by air currents; and (b) to shield the electroscope from neighboring charged objects.

Many years after Bennet's invention Michael Faraday (1791-1867), English physicist, showed that a glass-enclosed electroscope must be grounded in order to be trustworthy. Your glass-jar electroscope will be ungrounded. But for the simple experiments you will make, it will be satisfactory. However the electroscope enclosed in the coffee can will prove to be a superior instrument if you ground it as directed.

Note: Be sure to wind silk thread around the stem of the electroscope where it meets the paraffin wax so as to reduce leakage. The sealing-wax plug in the coffee can needs no extra insulation because sealing wax is an excellent insulator.

WHAT TO DO

. . . *making an aluminum-leaf electroscope*

1. Gilbert's **versorium**

DO THIS

a. Cut out an arrow-shaped piece of aluminum foil, or use the thin aluminum of a disposable aluminum pie-plate.

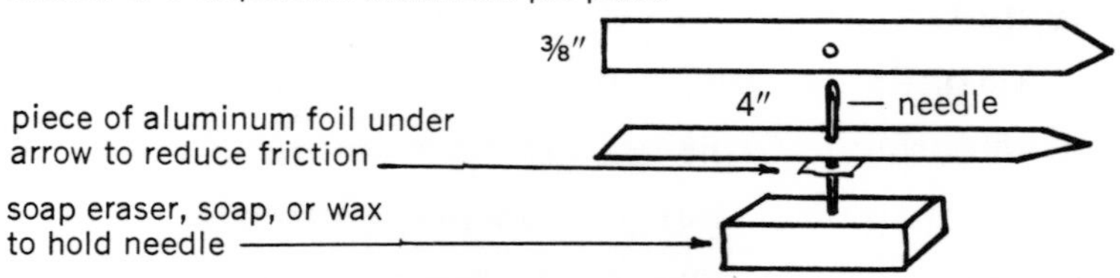

b. Electrify these and other materials by friction. Bring each close to the arrow. Is the pivoted arrow attracted? Explain.

hard-rubber comb (fur, wool)
inflated rubber balloon (wool)
wooden ruler (fur, wool)
plastic ruler (fur, wool)
bottom of glass jar (silk)
strip of newspaper (draw through fingers)
strip of plastic "wrap" (draw through fingers)

2. Prepare aluminum leaves for your electroscope. Make two sets. Follow directions exactly.

a. Use the thin aluminum foil from a chewing-gum wrapper. Soak to remove paper backing, if necessary.

b. Cut a strand of wire from lampcord. Run it through the holes in your aluminum leaves. Now make a double loop or the shape of an eight (8). Be sure the holes are wide enough so that leaves move without binding.

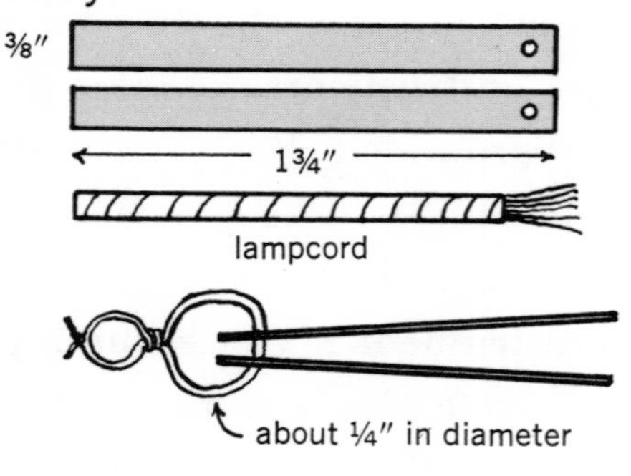

c. Cut 2 pieces of copper rod or #14 copper wire. Bend as indicated.

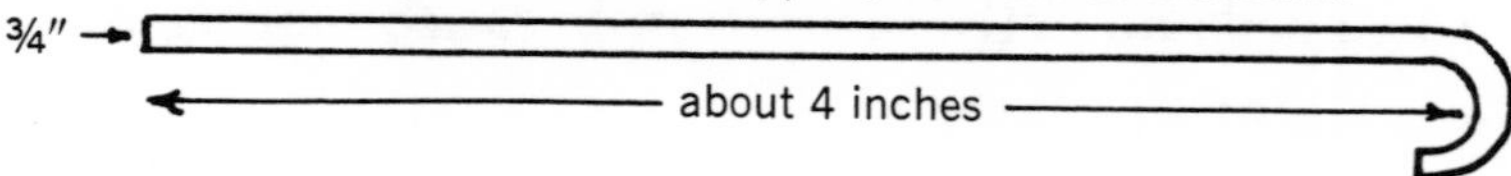

3. Enclose your electroscope in a pint jar.

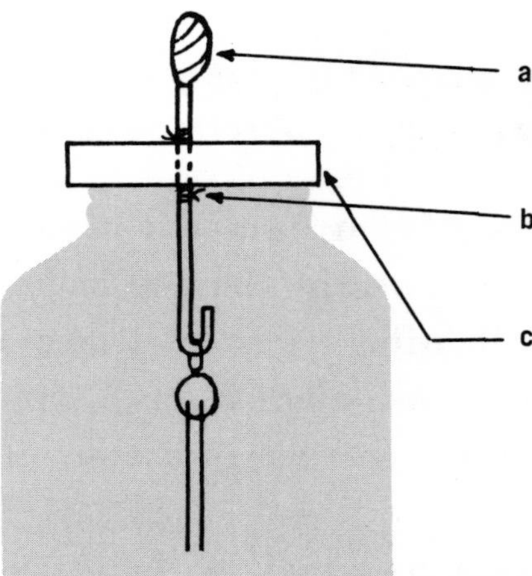

a. Curling the end and then covering it with smooth aluminum foil **may** improve your electroscope. Try it.

b. Wrap silk thread around rod or wire where it is in contact with the wax disk.

c. Cut disk out of block of paraffin wax to fit mouth of jar.

4. Your electroscope will be **more reliable** if it is enclosed in a metal container, preferably grounded.

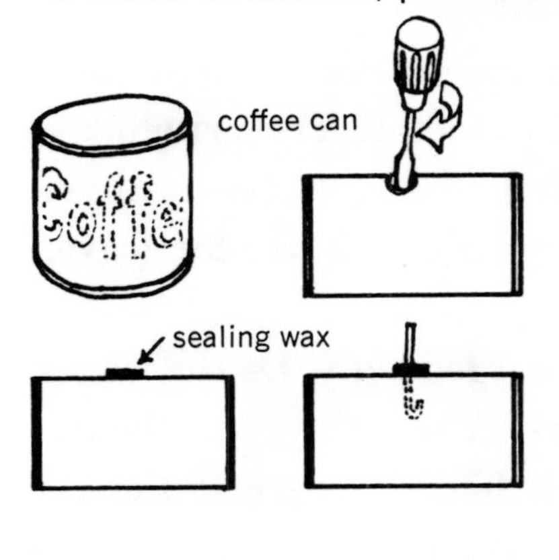

a. Punch a hole in the side of a coffee can. Insert screwdriver or file and twist to make hole about ½″ wide.

b. Soften sealing wax in candle flame and fill in the hole you made in the can. Then, **quickly**, while the sealing wax is still soft, push the copper rod from 2c through the wax from the inside of the can. Hold steady until the wax hardens.

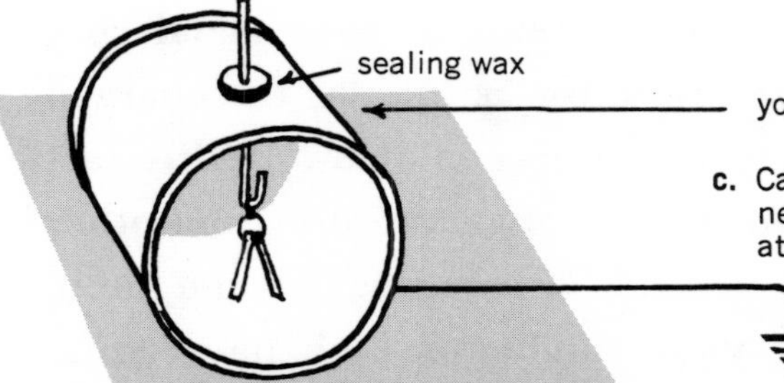

your coffee-can electroscope

c. Can is grounded by wire connected to waterpipe or radiator.

WHAT YOU SHOULD KNOW

...about electrifying a conductor by induction

You are going to electrify an insulated metal conductor by the influence of a nearby charged body. For this experiment you will utilize your electroscope. It is a metal conductor; it is insulated; it has aluminum leaves attached to one end to serve as indicators of the presence of an electric charge.

This method of electrifying a body without friction and without contact is called induction, or *electrostatic induction.*

You will begin with an uncharged electroscope, that is, an uncharged insulated conductor. Try bringing a charged body, such as sealing wax or a hard-rubber comb, *near* the knob of the electroscope. Do the leaves diverge? Why?

You will now remove the charged body. Do the leaves fall together once more? Why? You will repeat the experiment with other charged bodies to see if the response is the same as when sealing wax is used.

It is apparent that the far end of your metal conductor is in a charged state for as long as the charged body is held close to the near end. How is this fact explained? The atoms in copper, aluminum, and other metals are normally neutral. This means that the knob, wire, and leaves of your conductor each have equal amounts of positive and negative charge.

When the negatively charged sealing wax is brought near the knob of your electroscope, the electric field around the sealing wax exerts a force on the electrons in the knob. Some of these electrons are repelled. Since the atoms of all metals have some free electrons, these mobile particles move away from the knob and towards the leaves. The aluminum leaves then diverge. Why?

You have thus charged the far end of your conductor negatively by induction. Does this imply that the near end has, at the same time, been charged positively by induction?

When the sealing wax is removed from the vicinity of the knob, the mobile "extra" electrons return to the atoms from which they had been driven by the influence of the charged body. Now your conductor is neutral again.

Note that *no* electrons entered or left the conductor during the entire process. While the charged body was nearby, the far end acquired a charge of the same kind as that on the inducing body and the near end a charge of the opposite kind. Why?

It is true that the induced charges in this case are of a temporary nature. However, it is possible to produce a more-lasting charge in your electroscope, also by induction, by a method soon to be explained (see page 46).

Try to explain what happens when a positively charged body is substituted for the negative sealing wax in this experiment.

WHAT TO DO

...*charging the ends of a conductor by induction*

1. What happens when an electrified object is brought close to the knob of your electroscope? (Our diagrams will show only the essential parts of the electroscope.)

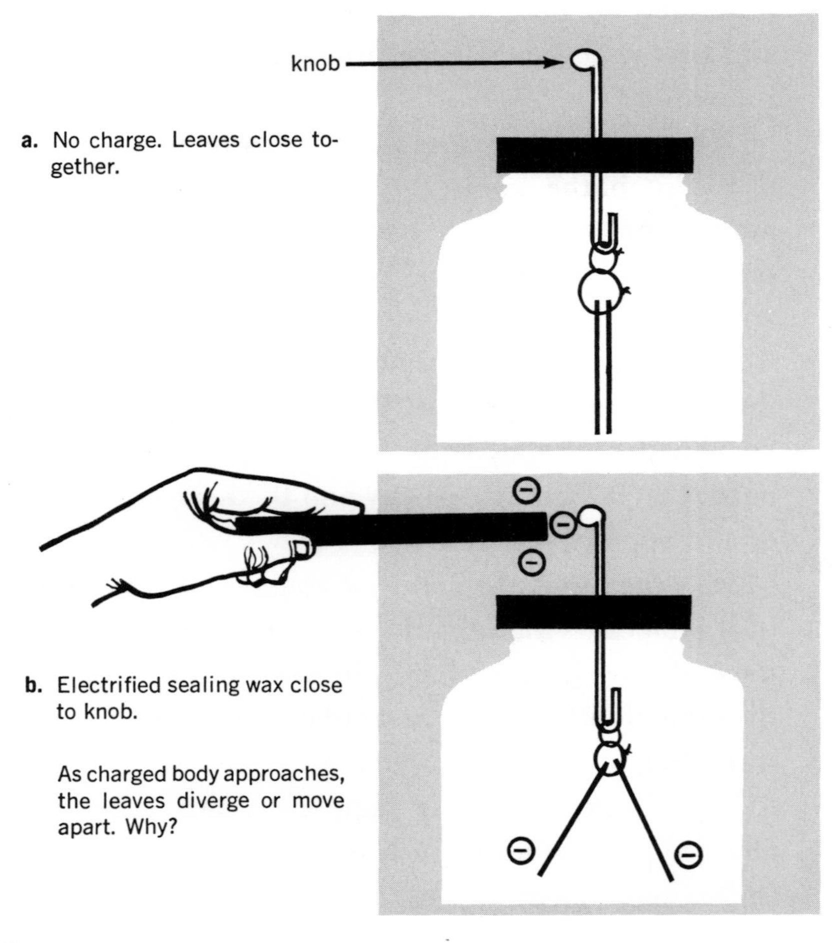

a. No charge. Leaves close together.

b. Electrified sealing wax close to knob.

As charged body approaches, the leaves diverge or move apart. Why?

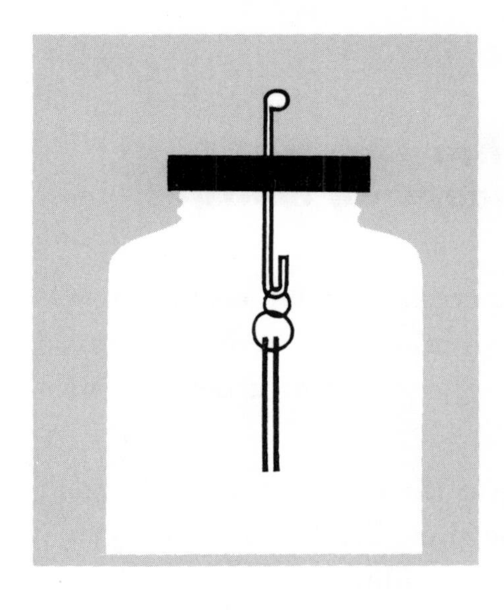

c. Aluminum leaves come together again when charged sealing wax is removed.

d. Ground your sealing wax by touching rubbed end with finger. Now bring neutral sealing wax near electroscope. What happens? Why?

2. Try same experiment with electrified glass rod (silk), or use bottom of a glass jar (silk).

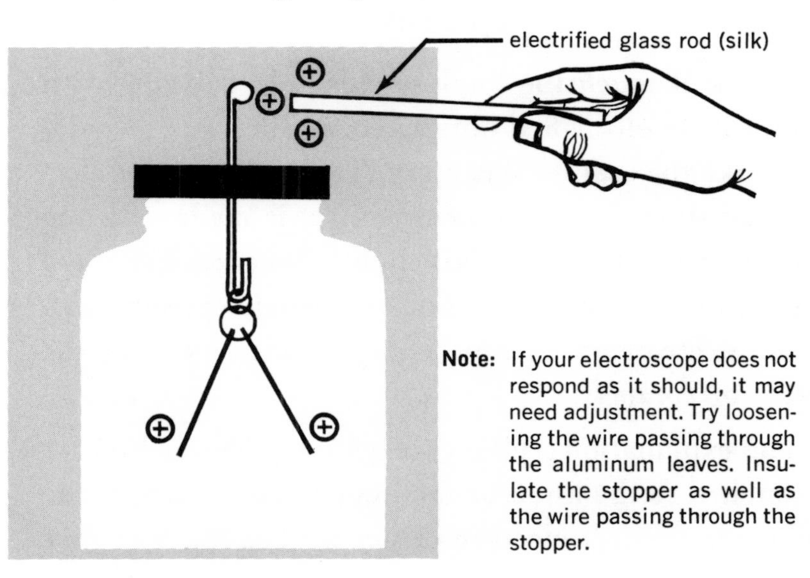

Note: If your electroscope does not respond as it should, it may need adjustment. Try loosening the wire passing through the aluminum leaves. Insulate the stopper as well as the wire passing through the stopper.

WHAT YOU SHOULD KNOW

...about charging an electroscope by contact

In the last series of experiments your electroscope was uncharged at the beginning and remained uncharged at the end. It merely served as a detector of electricity.

Now you are going to give the electroscope a charge that it will retain for some time. This means that you will either add electrons to, or subtract them from, the metal parts of the electroscope. As a result, the electroscope itself will be left with either a negative or positive charge.

You will *touch* the knob of your electroscope with a negatively electrified object like sealing wax (wool), then take the sealing wax away. The leaves of the electroscope diverge the moment contact is made with the sealing wax. The leaves fall slightly when the charged sealing wax is removed — but still remain spread apart. Your electroscope is now charged *negatively* as the result of *contact*.

The explanation? When a negatively charged object is touched to the knob of the neutral electroscope, the following occurs: electrons from the sealing wax flow into the knob, wire and leaves of the electroscope. These added electrons stay or are "locked in" when contact is broken.

The knob, wire and leaves now have an excess of electrons, or negative charges. These extra charges distribute themselves. The leaves get their share and show it by diverging because of mutual repulsion. This is why your electroscope now has a negative charge.

Now suppose you bring an object with an unknown charge up to your negatively charged electroscope. If the leaves diverge *still more* then the charge on this object must be *negative.* Why? Because a negatively charged object will repel more electrons from the knob to the leaves and thus increase the divergence.

Suppose the leaves fall close together at the approach of an unknown charge? Then you may conclude that the charge on the object must be *positive.* Why? Because a positive charge on the object will *attract* electrons from the leaves. As a result the leaves lose electrons, become *less negative*, and therefore repel each other with *less force.* Thus their divergence decreases, that is, they move closer together.

Try working out a similar explanation for an electroscope which, at the beginning, has a positive rather than a negative charge.

Tip about the experiments which follow:

Be sure to ground the knob by touching it with your finger before each new experiment.

WHAT TO DO

...how to charge an electroscope negatively

1. Try the contact method first.

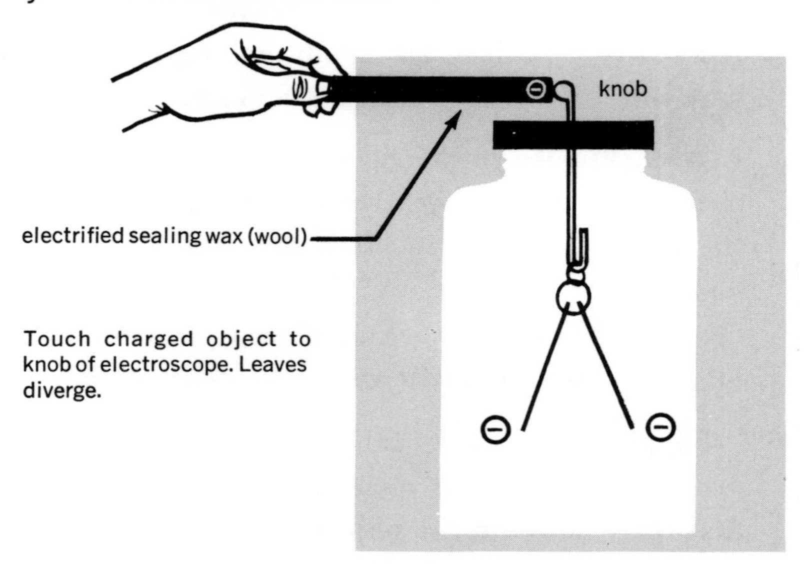

Touch charged object to knob of electroscope. Leaves diverge.

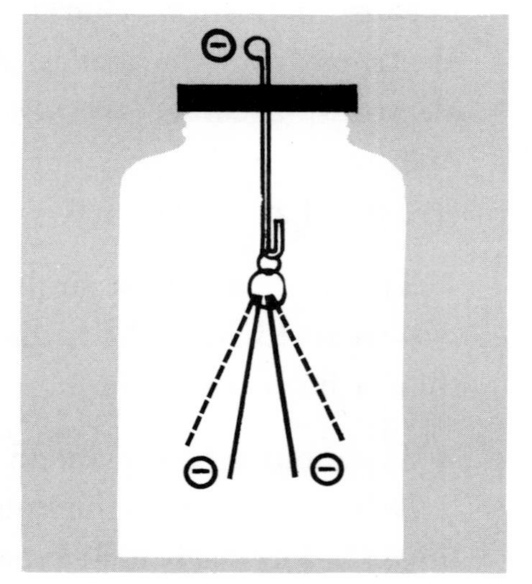

The electroscope now has a **negative** charge.

Take charged body away. Leaves fall slightly, but remain apart.

2. We can now use our **negatively charged** electroscope to determine the sign, + or −, of the charge on **any** electrified body.

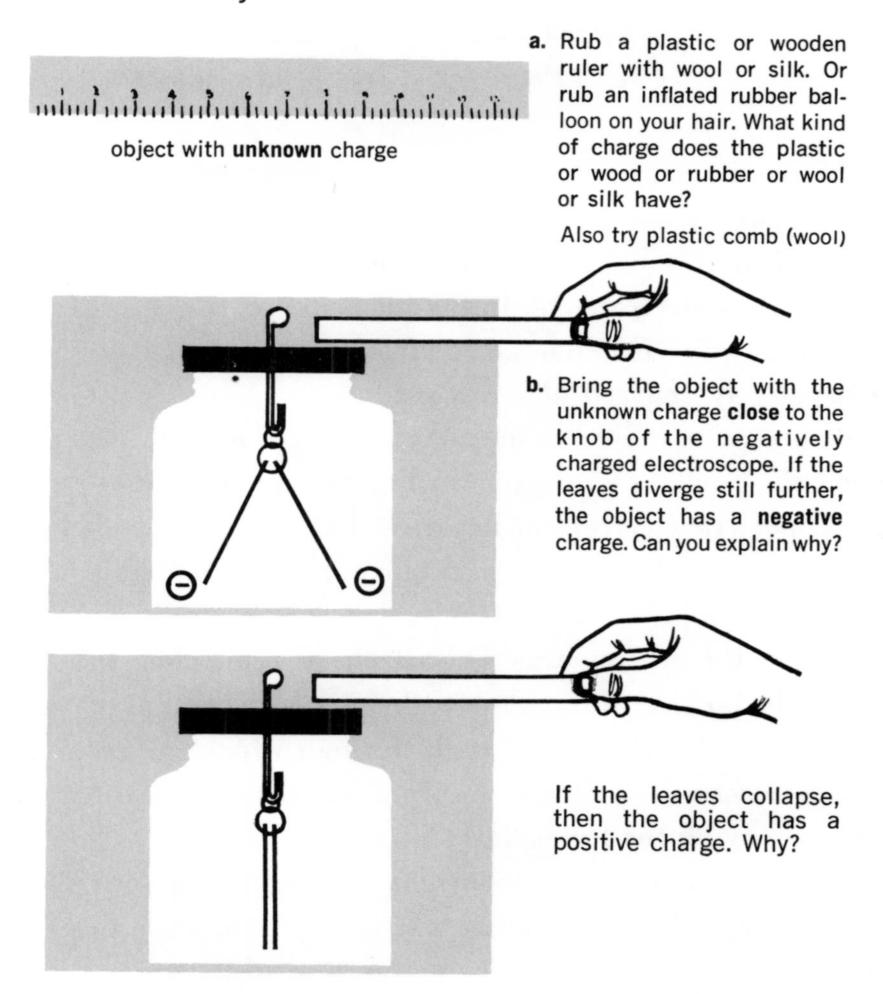

a. Rub a plastic or wooden ruler with wool or silk. Or rub an inflated rubber balloon on your hair. What kind of charge does the plastic or wood or rubber or wool or silk have?

Also try plastic comb (wool)

b. Bring the object with the unknown charge **close** to the knob of the negatively charged electroscope. If the leaves diverge still further, the object has a **negative** charge. Can you explain why?

If the leaves collapse, then the object has a positive charge. Why?

3. Ground your electroscope by touching knob with finger. Now try to give it a **positive** charge by contact, using a glass rod (silk).

WHAT YOU SHOULD KNOW

...about charging an electroscope by induction

In the next experiments, you are going to charge your electroscope by causing some electrons to flow either from the electroscope to the earth, *or* from the earth to the electroscope. In the former case, the result will be a positively charged electroscope; in the latter, a negatively charged electroscope.

You are going to bring a negatively charged object, like electrified sealing wax, *near* the knob of a *neutral* electroscope. The electrons or negative charges in the knob will be repelled as before and move as far as possible from the knob.

While the sealing wax is *still close*, remember to touch the far side of the knob with a finger. Your finger and body will then form a path through which the repelled electrons will escape from the leaves to the earth. Why do the leaves fall?

The next step is *very important*. You will take your finger away *while* the sealing wax is still held close to the knob. This will break the connection to the earth. The electrons that escaped to the earth *cannot get back*. Your electroscope is left with a *deficiency* of electrons and is therefore *positively* charged.

Finally, when the charged sealing wax is removed, the leaves diverge and stay diverged. In this manner, you have charged your electroscope *positively* by induction. The entire electroscope — knob, wire and leaves — now has a deficiency of electrons. Why?

Notice that charging by induction results in a charge *opposite* to that of the original charge. A *negatively charged* body will induce a *positive charge* in an electroscope; a *positively charged* body will induce a *negative* charge in an electroscope.

Try charging an electroscope *negatively* by induction. Use a charged glass rod (rubbed with silk). Try working out an explanation similar to the one given above. In this case, electrons *from the earth* will flow into the leaves of the electroscope.

When charging by induction always remember to remove the finger *first*, and *then* the charged object. Why?

In charging by induction it is the earth that gains or loses electrons. The electric field around the charged object prevents the electrons from returning to the electroscope or to the earth. To cut off the return path, the finger must be removed *before* taking the charged object away.

Hint about the experiments which follow:

Try using a hard-rubber comb (wool) or an inflated rubber balloon (rubbed on your dry hair) to charge an electroscope by induction. Also try giving a pith ball a charge by induction, using the method similar to that described above.

WHAT TO DO

...another way of charging an electroscope

1. How to charge an electroscope by induction.

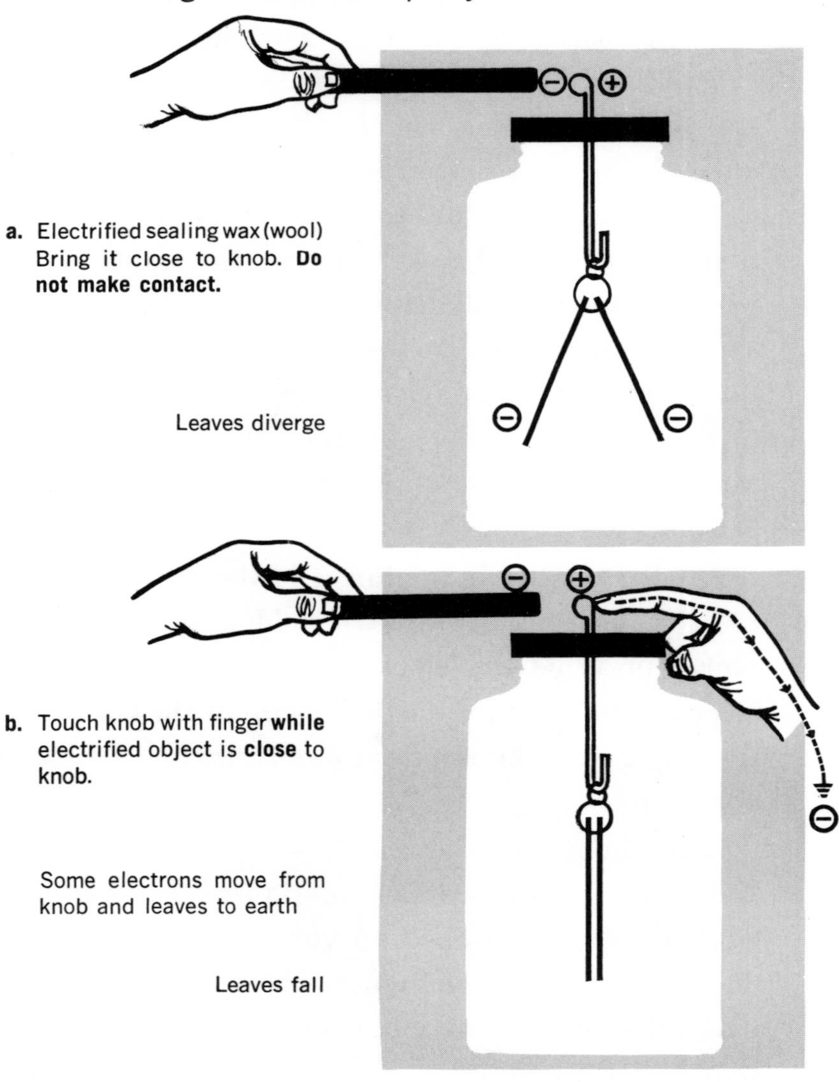

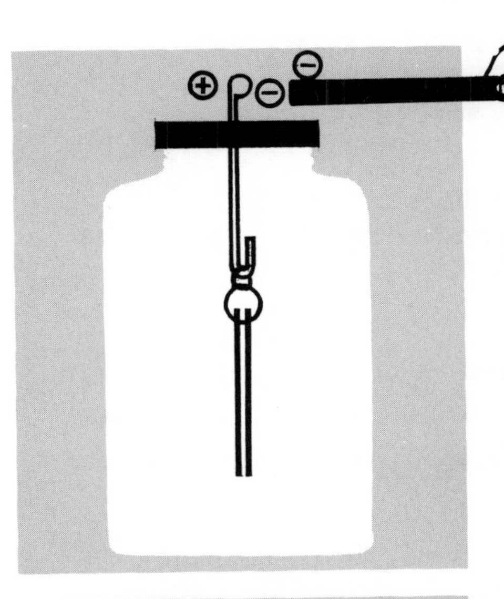

c. Keep electrified object **near** knob — but **remove** finger from knob.

Now the connection with the earth is broken. Electrons which left the electroscope cannot return.

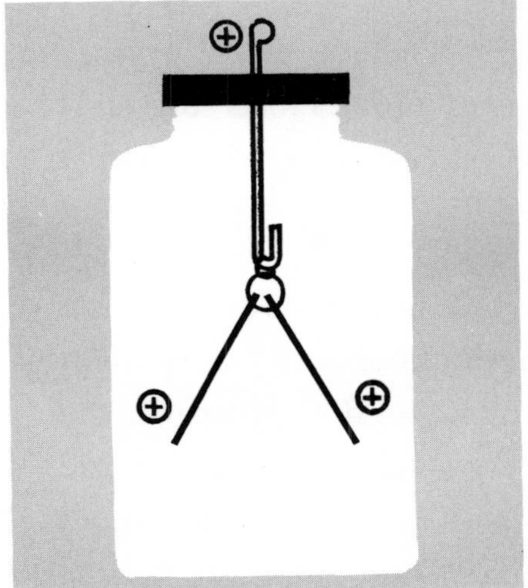

d. Now **remove** electrified object.

Leaves move apart. Each has a deficiency of electrons and is therefore positive.

WHAT YOU SHOULD KNOW

...about using a charged electroscope to distinguish between positive and negative charges

In the last series of experiments we stated that the negatively electrified sealing wax gave your electroscope a positive charge by induction. Let's prove that it did.

First, you will charge your electroscope inductively, using the electrified sealing wax as before. Now a piece of negatively charged sealing wax is brought up to the charged electroscope.

The leaves of your electroscope are in a diverged position at first. As the negatively charged sealing wax approaches the knob, the leaves move closer together or even collapse. Thus, the leaves must have had a *positive* charge.

The explanation? The electric field around the sealing wax repels electrons from the knob and forces them down into the leaves. These additional electrons in the leaves cancel, or neutralize, the positive charges there. The leaves then become *less unlike*; that is, they repel one another with *less* force.

Therefore, we can say that the leaves of a charged electroscope will collapse when an *unlike* charge approaches. This fact is used to identify an unknown charge on any object.

Suppose a *positively* charged object, such as an electrified glass rod (silk), is brought near the knob of a *positively* charged electroscope.

Electrons will be *attracted* to the knob from the leaves because of the field around the charged glass. The leaves, in losing electrons, become more *positive*: they will diverge or move apart even farther than before.

Therefore, we say that the leaves of a charged electroscope will *diverge farther* when a *like* charge approaches the knob.

What if the electroscope has a negative charge to begin with? Can you explain what happens when a positively charged hard-rubber comb (wool) approaches the knob? Try it.

Note about the experiments which follow:
Try touching or grounding the knob of a charged electroscope. Why do the leaves collapse at once? Try folding a large sheet of plastic material into several layers, each about 6″ x 6″. Rub the upper surface with silk. What charge is on the plastic? On the silk? Use your charged electroscope to find out.

WHAT TO DO

. . . using a charged electroscope to identify the charges on electrified objects

1. Suppose you used negatively charged sealing wax to charge your electroscope by induction. How can you prove that the aluminum leaves have a positive charge?

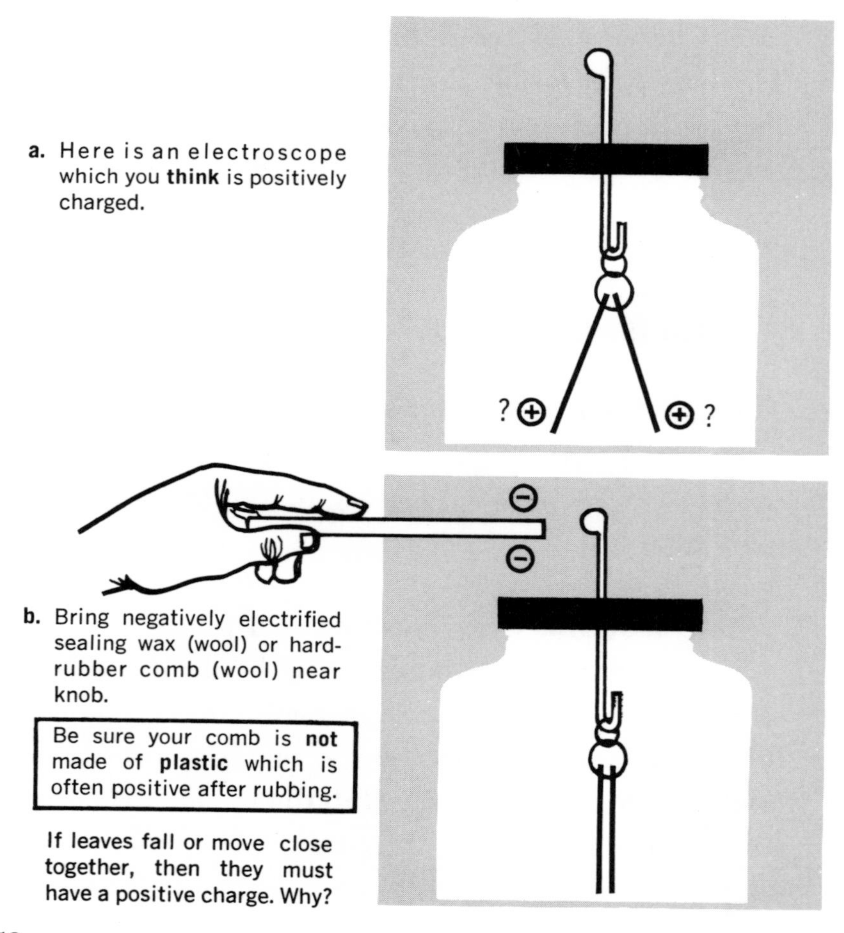

a. Here is an electroscope which you **think** is positively charged.

b. Bring negatively electrified sealing wax (wool) or hard-rubber comb (wool) near knob.

> Be sure your comb is **not** made of **plastic** which is often positive after rubbing.

If leaves fall or move close together, then they must have a positive charge. Why?

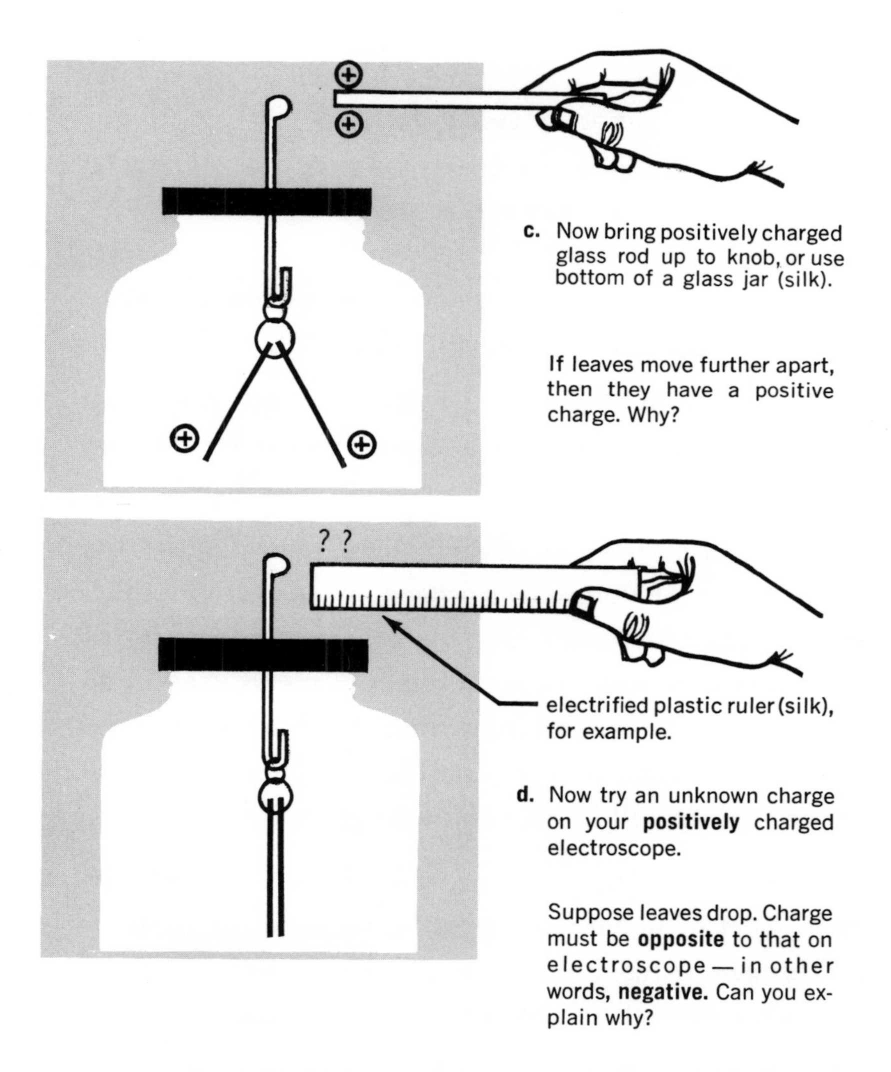

c. Now bring positively charged glass rod up to knob, or use bottom of a glass jar (silk).

If leaves move further apart, then they have a positive charge. Why?

electrified plastic ruler (silk), for example.

d. Now try an unknown charge on your **positively** charged electroscope.

Suppose leaves drop. Charge must be **opposite** to that on electroscope — in other words, **negative.** Can you explain why?

2. Is the charge on the wool with which you rubbed the sealing wax or hard-rubber comb positive or negative? Bring it near an electroscope with a known charge and find out as explained above. Grasp wool cloth with insulator. (See note on page 29.)

WHAT YOU SHOULD KNOW

...about making an electrophorus or simple electric generator

The electrophorus was invented by a famous Italian physicist, Alessandro Volta (1745-1827).

The principle of the electrophorus is utilized in all electrostatic machines which generate electricity by *induction*.

In the last series of experiments, you charged the metal leaves of your electroscope by *induction*. Likewise, in the electrophorus you will charge a sheet of metal by *induction*. Since the sheet of metal used in an electrophorus is much larger than the small aluminum leaves of an electroscope, the electric charge induced on the former will be correspondingly greater.

To make an electrophorus, you can use either a circular sheet of metal such as an aluminum pie plate or an aluminum ice tray. As long as the surface of the conductor is slightly *irregular*, it will work.

Since the metal sheet must be moved, it needs an insulating handle. Otherwise, any charge on the sheet will be neutralized by your body the moment the sheet is raised. This must be prevented.

An insulating handle can be made by attaching a piece of sealing wax or candle to the center of the metal plate or tray. Do this by first heating the metal and then touching the sealing wax or candle to it. When the melted sealing wax or candle solidifies, it should adhere firmly to the metal.

When you charged an electroscope by induction you held a charged object, like electrified sealing wax, *near* the metal knob of your electroscope.

In your electrophorus the charged object will be a large flat piece of sealing wax *or* hard rubber *or* glass *or* plastic sheet — *or* any good insulator which has been *electrified by friction.* If, as suggested, a large thick, folded piece of plastic sheet is used, try to charge it by rubbing with silk.

How did you charge an electroscope by induction? An electrified object was brought near the knob; you grounded the knob by touching it with your finger; you removed your finger and *then* the electrified object. The result was that the leaves of the electroscope acquired an electric charge by *induction.*

As you will soon see, the method of charging the *metal* sheet of an electrophorus *by induction* is similar to that used in charging an electroscope *by induction.*

Tip about the experiments which follow:
You may also attach an insulating handle of wood or plastic by means of a nail or screw through the center of the metal plate or tray.

WHAT TO DO

...making an electrophorus or a simple electric generator

1. Here is the type of electrophorus used in your science class:

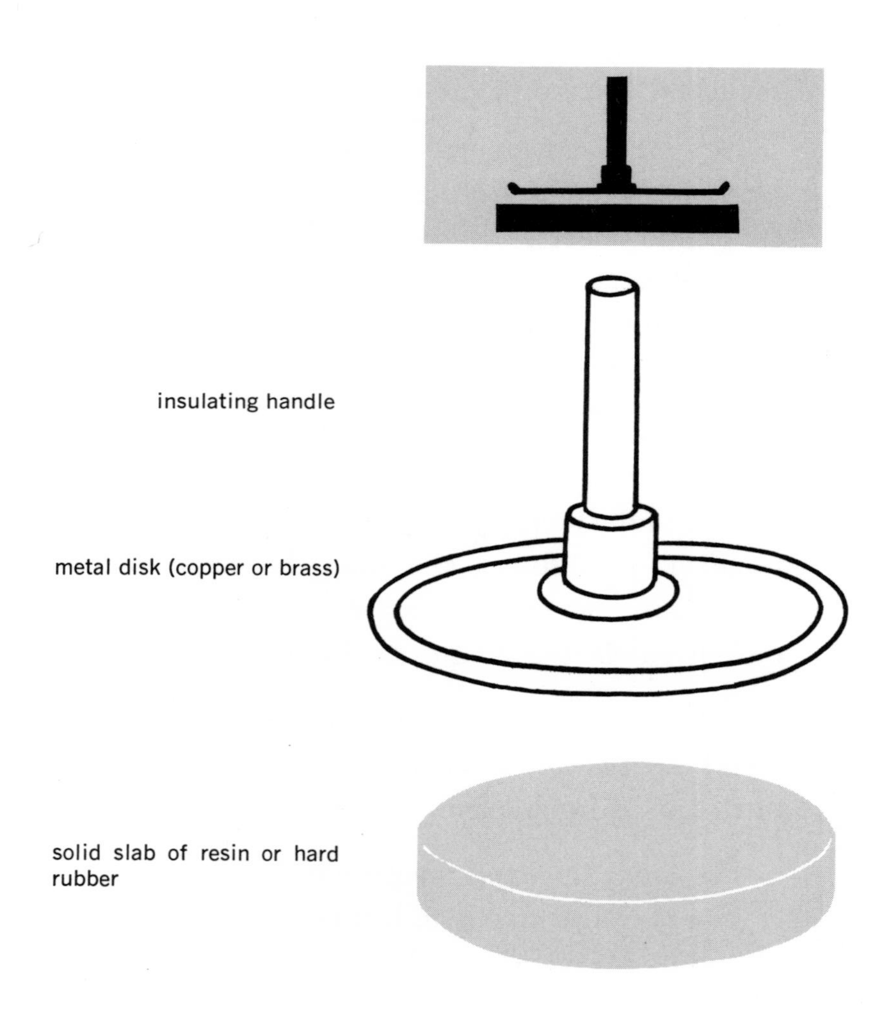

2. What you can use to make an electrophorus at home:

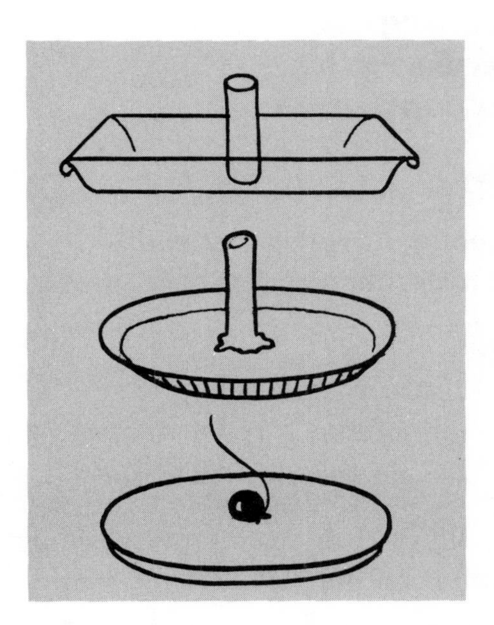

a. Instead of a circular metal plate you may substitute one of any one of these:

attached candle

aluminum ice cube tray

candle serves as insulating handle

aluminum pie plate

silk thread instead of candle

silk thread tied to knob of an aluminum pot cover

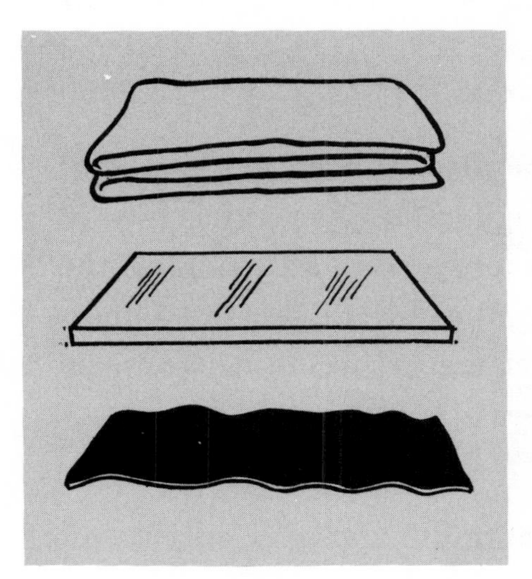

b. Instead of hard rubber or resin base use one of these:

Sheet of plastic (polyethylene) folded into several thicknesses. This type of plastic sheet is used for storm windows. It stretches when pulled.

or use

sheet of glass

or use

sheet of rubber from old inner tube

WHAT YOU SHOULD KNOW

...about charging and discharging an electrophorus

You are going to produce an electric charge on a folded plastic sheet by rubbing its surface with silk. If you are using glass, rub it with silk, too. A rubber sheet should be rubbed with wool.

You will then grasp the aluminum tray by its insulating handle and set it down on the electrified sheet.

While the aluminum tray is on the plastic sheet, you will momentarily touch the edge of the tray with your finger and thus ground it.

Now lift the tray off the plastic sheet, being careful to touch *only* the insulating handle. The tray is now in a charged state. You can prove this by bringing the edge of the tray near a metallic object like a brass doorknob. Do you see and hear a spark jump between the edge of the tray and the brass knob?

After the spark, your aluminum tray is once again

uncharged, or neutral. It should then be set on the plastic sheet a second time and grounded by touching an edge with your finger. Next, the tray is lifted into the air again. This time try bringing your knuckle near its edge. Do you see and feel a spark?

Your aluminum tray can be recharged many times by simply placing it on the electrified plastic sheet and grounding the tray with a finger. When your spark becomes small or short, it is a sign that the plastic sheet needs to be rubbed again.

You may ask why the above method is called charging by *induction* when the metal and plastic appear to be in actual contact during the charging process.

The answer is this: Examine the two surfaces which are seemingly in close contact. The plastic surface is irregular; the bottom of the aluminum is also irregular. There are only relatively few points where aluminum actually *touches* plastic. Most of the metal surface is *close to* but not in contact with the plastic.

Tip about the experiments which follow:

If you have trouble attaching the insulating handle to the tray, do this: instead of a tray, use a clean, *grease-free* aluminum pot cover which can be raised or lowered by means of a silk thread tied to the center knob.

WHAT TO DO

...learning how to use your electrophorus

1. Charging an electrophorus.

a. Rub folded polyethylene sheet vigorously 20 to 30 times with silk (or use glass plate or sheet of inner tube rubber)

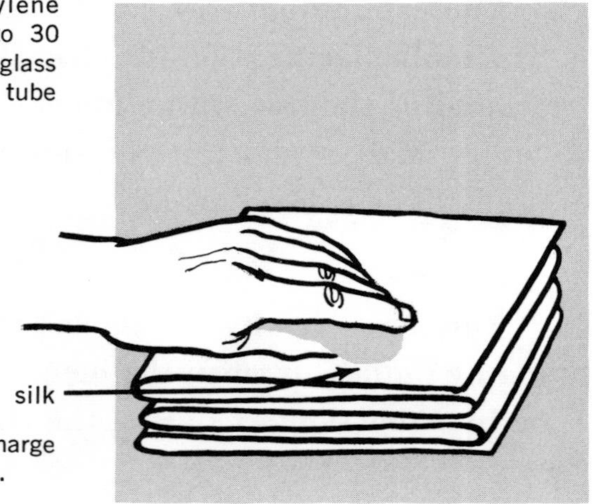

Producing an electric charge on insulator by friction.

b. Plastic sheet now has a strong negative charge.

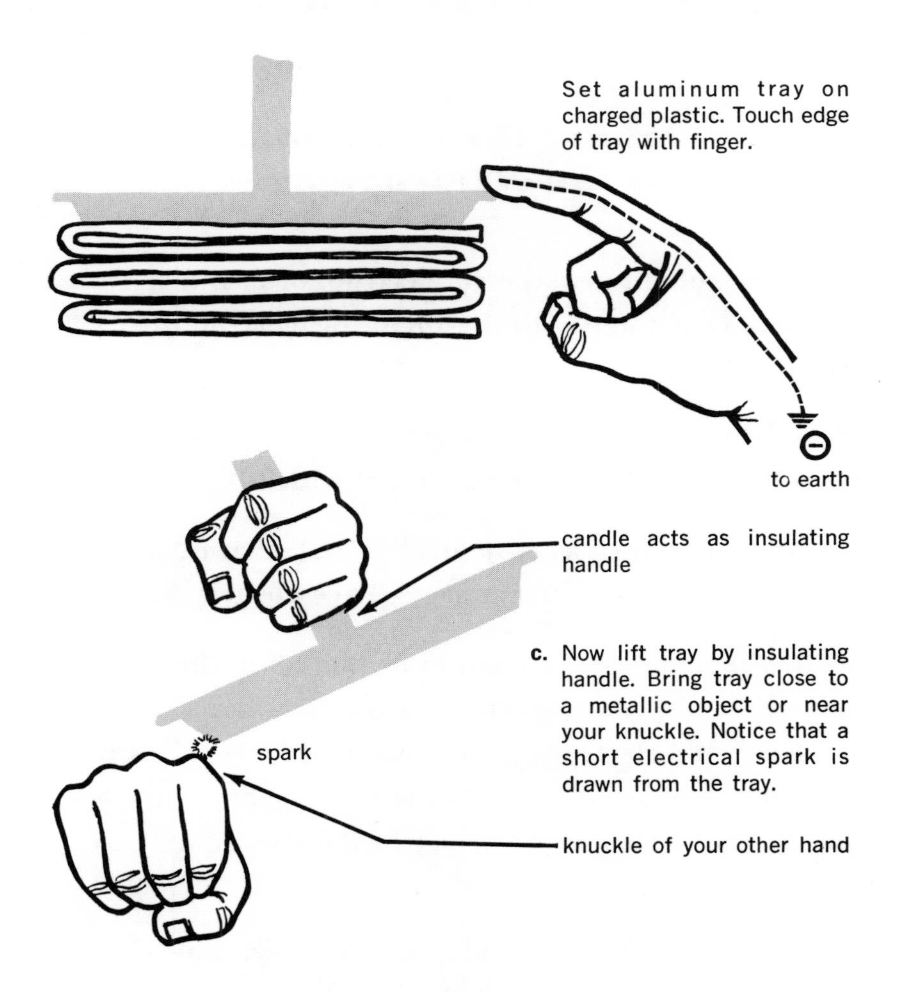

2. Repeat and draw another spark. This means returning the tray to the charged plastic, grounding tray as before by touching it with finger, and then lifting tray into the air again. This may be repeated many times before plastic has to be recharged by rubbing.

WHAT YOU SHOULD KNOW

...about the explanation of the electrophorus

You are going to charge an electrophorus and try to understand each step with the aid of the electron theory (See page 26).

First you will produce a negative charge on the surface of the plastic sheet by rubbing it with silk.

Your aluminum tray is neutral at first, that is, it has equal amounts of positive and negative electricity.

Now your neutral tray should be placed on the negatively charged plastic sheet. By *induction,* some *negative* charges or electrons in the tray will be repelled to the upper surface of the aluminum. The *positive* charges stay on the lower surface of the aluminum tray or close to the charged plastic.

Then try touching the edge of the tray. The electrons on the tray's upper surface will escape through your body to the earth. Why? Because they are repelled by the negatively charged plastic sheet.

When you take your finger off the tray, the tray, having lost electrons to the *earth*, is now *cut off* from the earth. Your tray thus acquires a *positive* charge, that is, it has a *deficiency* of electrons.

Now try raising the aluminum tray, with its positive charge, into the air by its insulating handle. Then bring the edge of the tray near a metal object or your own knuckle. Do you observe a spark?

The spark is caused by electrons from the metal object, or your knuckle, jumping across the air gap into the aluminum tray. After the spark, the aluminum tray is neutral once again. You can test it by bringing it up to a charged electroscope.

Why can this operation be repeated again and again without recharging the plastic sheet? Because *no charge* is taken from the plastic sheet during the entire process. The negative charges on the plastic sheet merely *repel* electrons in the aluminum each time the tray is placed on the plastic.

The spark produced in discharging the aluminum tray is accompanied by heat and sound. Where does the energy for this come from? The answer is from *you;* that is, the work done by you in lifting the tray from the plastic sheet. It requires *work* to separate the two charged surfaces.

Note about the experiments which follow:

Try to explain the charging process when a positively charged sheet of glass (silk) is substituted for the negatively charged plastic sheet in the above experiments.

WHAT TO DO

. . . *understanding how an electrophorus "works"*

1. Go over the charging process one step at a time.

a. Suppose the insulator—plastic or rubber or sealing wax — becomes negatively electrified when rubbed.

electrified sheet (plastic, hard rubber, etc.)

b. Set the metal plate on the electrified material. By induction, some minus charges in the metal plate are repelled to upper surface of the metal.

Contact surfaces are bumpy or irregular.

c. Finger grounds metal plate. The electrons or negative charges are repelled to the earth by way of finger and body.

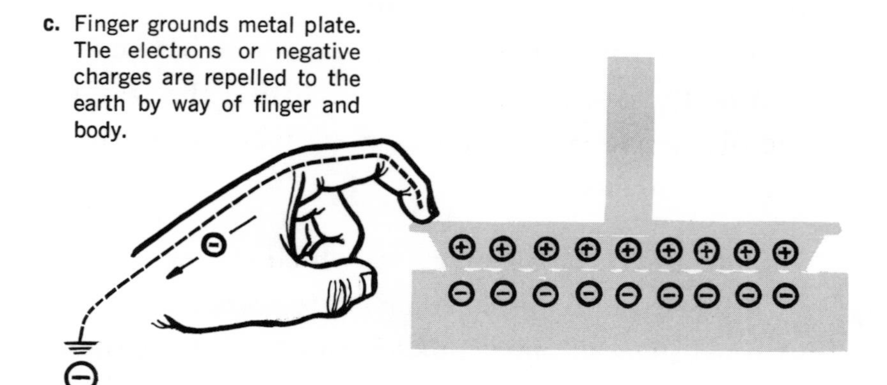

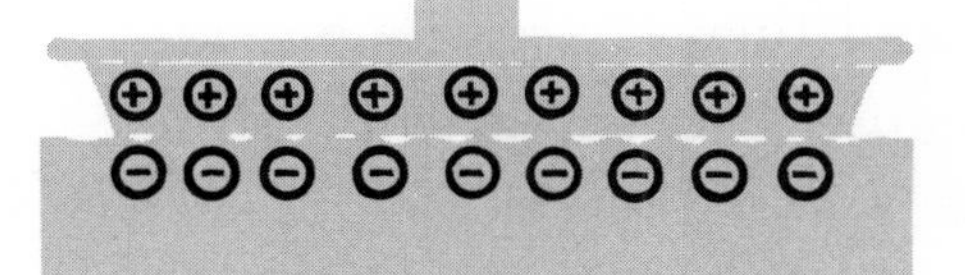

d. Now remove finger. This breaks the connection with the earth. The plate is left with a plus charge, that is, a deficiency of electrons.

e. Remove plate by insulating handle. Bring your knuckle close to edge of plate. Do you feel and see a spark?

Electrons rush from hand into plate, making plate neutral again.

2. Set plate on your plastic again. Touch finger to it. Lift and apply knuckle to plate. Do you see a spark? Repeat this several times.

WHAT YOU SHOULD KNOW

...*about electrostatic shielding*

You are going to place either a coffee can or a deep metal cup on an insulator and then charge its outside surface with an electrified object, as explained on the following pages.

A proof plane is a simple device used to test or transfer small electric charges. You will touch the proof plane to the outside of the can and then bring the proof plane in contact with an electroscope. You will find that the *outside* of the can is charged.

You will then test the inside of the can in the same way after completely discharging the proof plane by touching it with your finger. This time you will find that the *inside* of the can shows no charge at all.

The charge on an electrical conductor is wholly on the *outside* surface. This is understandable because the charge you gave the can consists of many small charges which repel one another. The reason the charges end up on the outside of the can is that they tend to move as far apart as possible. Why?

In one of his famous experiments, Michael Faraday (page 35) built a chamber in the form of a 12-foot cube and covered the outside of the structure with tin foil. After insulating the chamber from the ground, he electrified the exterior intensely. Even with large sparks leaping on to the tin-foil exterior Faraday found that electroscopes *inside* the chamber were in no way affected by the external charge.

A charged conductor may thus be *shielded* from the influence of other conductors by enclosing the former in a metal case. A cage made of fine metal wire gauze will effectively shield an electroscope from nearby electrified bodies.

The important fact about electrostatic shielding is that any region enclosed by a conductor is entirely free from electrostatic fields *outside* the enclosure.

If you apply a thin coat of metallic paint to a sphere of pith or cork or any insulating material, the sphere will then conduct static charges as if it were made entirely of metal. Why?

Radio tubes sometimes have metal covers to prevent the intrusion of stray electrostatic fields. The steel frames of modern skyscrapers provide some measure of protection from lightning strokes. Why? Metal roofs connected to the moist ground also protect the interiors of buildings from lightning strokes to some degree. Try to explain the last statement.

WHAT TO DO

...using a metal case or screen to shield a charged conductor from external electrostatic fields

1. Make a proof plane and practice using it.

DO THIS

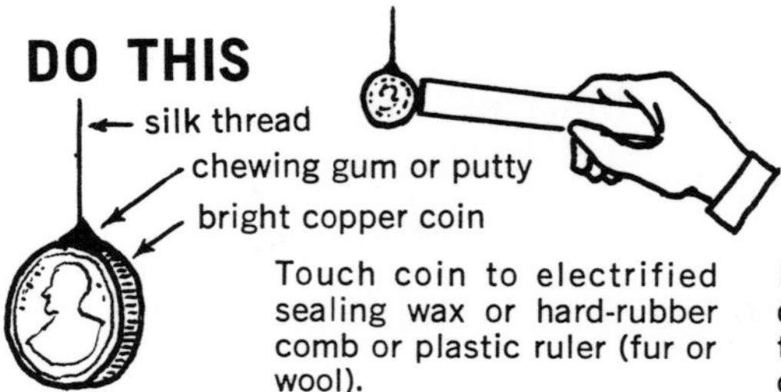

Touch coin to electrified sealing wax or hard-rubber comb or plastic ruler (fur or wool).

Now touch proof plane to charged electroscope. Did the proof plane carry a charge? Explain.

2. Charging a metal cup or can.

a. Rub electrified object, such as sealing wax or hard-rubber comb or plastic ruler on **outside** of can. Do this several times.

paraffin wax block (insulator)

b. Is outside of can charged?

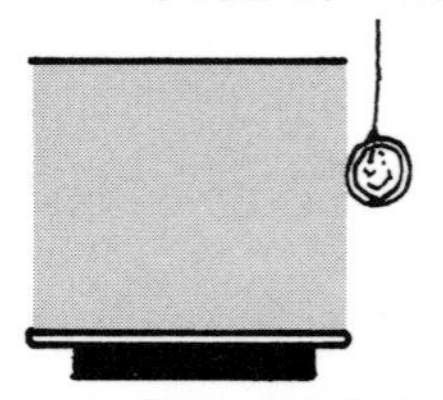

First discharge proof plane by touching coin with finger. Now let coin touch outside of can. Bring proof plane to charged electroscope.

proof plane

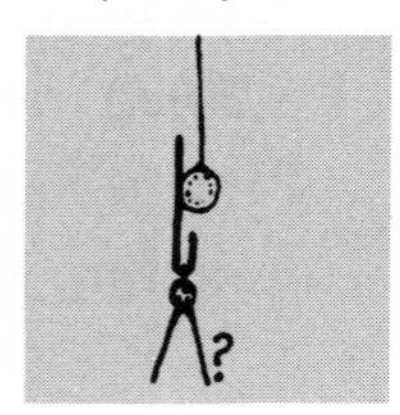

c. Does proof plane show a charge?

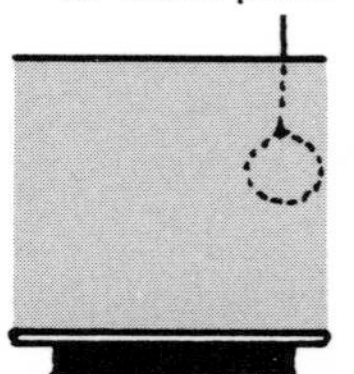

Touch coin with finger to discharge it. Now let it touch **inside** of can. Bring proof plane to charged electroscope again.

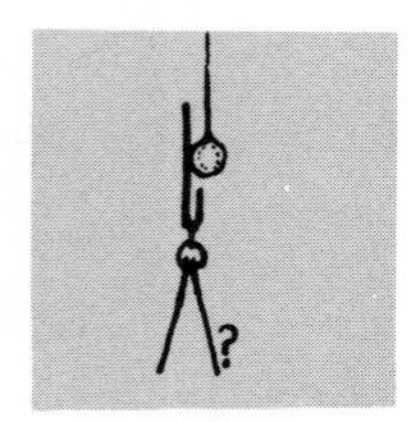

Any charge on inside of can?

3. Will the can act as a shield?

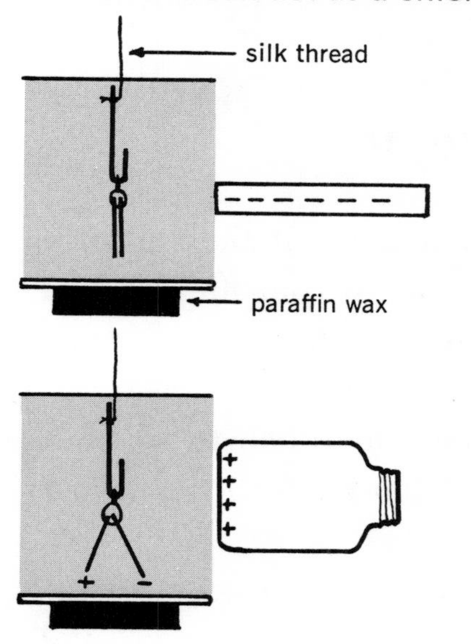

uncharged electroscope
(without case)

electrified sealing wax or hard rubber or plastic ruler

Can you charge the electroscope from the outside of the can? Try it.

Lower a charged electroscope into can. Will a charged glass jar (silk) affect it, or discharge it, through the can? Try it.

4. Shielding: Surround an electroscope (inside part only) with aluminum foil.

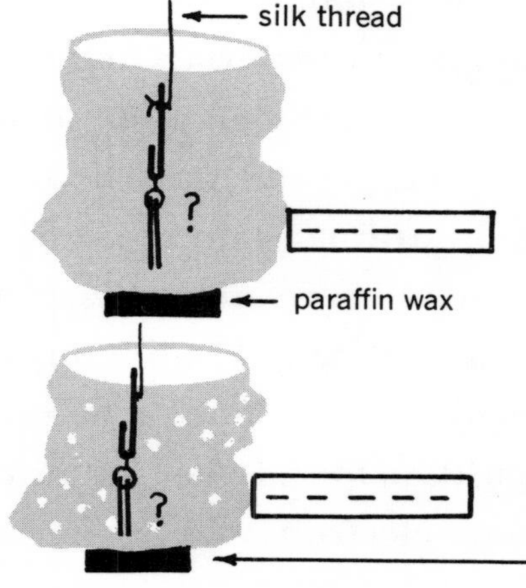

a. Charge the outside of the foil several times with electrified sealing wax or hard rubber or plastic ruler. Can you get the leaves to diverge? Explain. Lower a charged electroscope into interior and repeat. Explain.

b. Make many small holes in foil and repeat the above experiment. Will these perforations reduce the screening effect of the foil? Try it.

paraffin wax

5. Try a copper or aluminum screen around your electroscope instead of aluminum foil.

WHAT YOU SHOULD KNOW

...about the discharging effect of points

You are going to electrify a tassel at the end of a strip of newspaper by the friction of your fingers. You will then discharge each streamer by bringing a needle point up close to it.

You will also charge a brass doorknob to which a needle has been attached. The doorknob will soon lose its charge.

Dry air, like other gases, is almost a perfect insulator under normal conditions. As long as the air's atoms and molecules are electrically neutral, air remains a very poor conductor of electricity. However, the air of the atmosphere is always slightly *ionized* by cosmic rays and by radiation from radioactive materials in the earth.

Ionization is the process whereby an atom or molecule acquires an electric charge and thus becomes a conductor of electricity. In ordinary air about five ion pairs per cubic centimeter are formed each second at sea level. This occurs because external radiations cause some air atoms or molecules to lose one or more electrons and thus become *positive ions*. Other air atoms or molecules gain one or more electrons and become *negative ions*.

Suppose you gave the doorknob with needle attached

a strong negative charge. This charge will be denser, or more concentrated, at the needle point than on the rounded knob. The few positive ions in the air near the point begin to move towards the negatively charged point. On their way these ions collide with neutral air atoms and eject electrons from the latter. In this manner more negative and positive ions are quickly formed. The stream of positively charged ions, on reaching the negatively charged needle point, soon discharges or neutralizes the latter. Thus the brass doorknob gradually loses its charge.

The discharge process is similar in the case of the paper streamers. The needle point *you* hold near the charged streamer develops an opposite charge by electrostatic induction (page 30). Again ions move, collide, and form more ions. Soon positive ions are moving one way and negative ions the opposite way. Why? Very quickly the paper streamer falls: it has been discharged by the needle point. Explain this.

Vapors arising from a match flame or candle flame are usually ionized for a second or less. Try to explain why a match flame held near a charged electroscope will quickly discharge it.

Sometimes a heavily charged cloud will induce a large opposite charge on buildings lying below it. The sharp points of lightning rods tend to send this induced charge up into the air towards the cloud and thus help to discharge the cloud. Why? This silent discharge action is slow, however, and cannot be depended upon.

WHAT TO DO

...using a needle point to discharge an electrified body

1. Charge and then discharge a paper tassel.

DO THIS

a. Cut out of newspaper a strip about 10 inches long and 2 inches wide. Then cut into one end to form a tassel as shown.

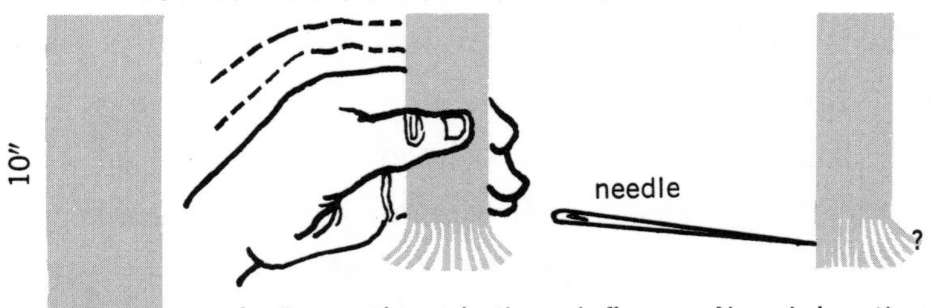

b. Run entire strip through fingers several times to charge it. Repulsion causes the strands to stand out.

c. Now bring the point of a needle opposite and close to **each** strand. Does each one collapse? Why?

2″ about 15 strands

2. Use a needle to discharge an electrified polished-brass doorknob.

a. Make a paper tassel
Use single thickness facial tissue.

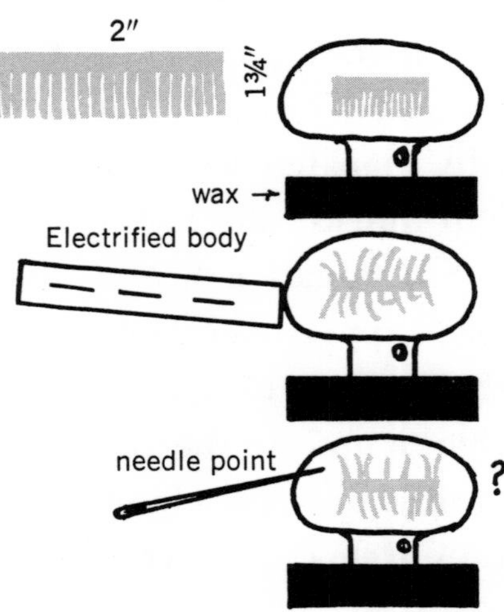

b. Attach tassel to doorknob with cellophane tape. Block of paraffin wax serves as insulator.

c. Touch **knob** with charged sealing wax or charged hard-rubber comb or charged plastic ruler. Touch charged body to different places on knob. Are strands repelled? Why?

d. Present needle point to each upstanding strand. Bring it close. Explain what happens.

3. Will attaching a sharp point to the brass knob in the previous experiment have any effect? Try it.

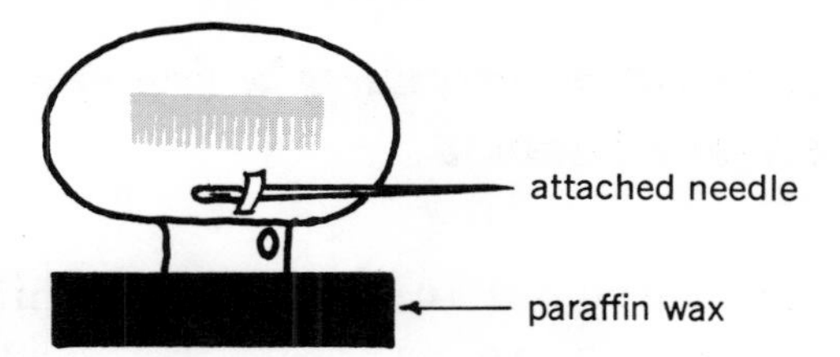

a. Using cellophane tape, attach a needle to the brass knob.

b. Try charging the knob as in 2c. Does the paper tassel respond? How long do the strands continue to stand up and repel one another now?

c. Check time elapsing before tassel loses its charge when needle is present and when needle is not present.

4. Discharging an electroscope by bringing needle point close to it.

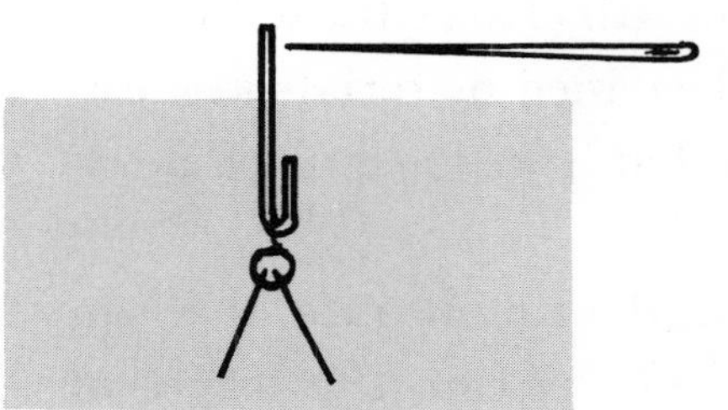

a. Charge an electroscope with your sealing wax or hard-rubber comb or plastic ruler.

b. Hold the point close. Will the leaves gradually fall? Try it. Be patient.

5. A faster method of discharging an electroscope: Bring a flame near the end of knob.

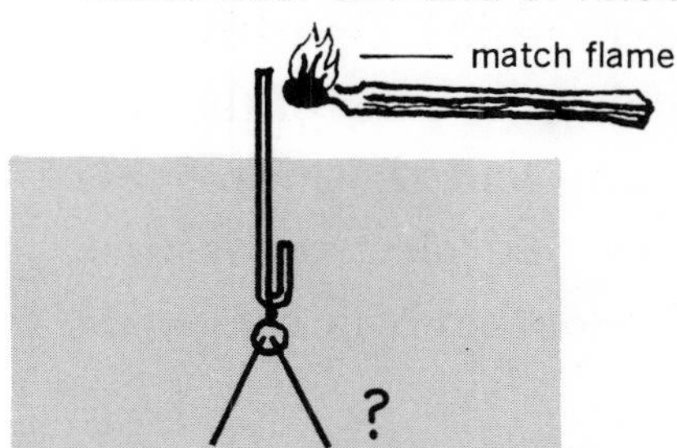

Do the leaves fall quickly? Why?

WHAT YOU SHOULD KNOW

...about Faraday's ice-pail experiment

You are going to carry out an experiment similar to the one Faraday made in 1810. This famous experiment proved that a charged body induces equal and opposite charges in conductors that completely surround it.

Faraday employed a pewter ice pail, but you will use either a coffee can or a large metal cup. Instead of a metal ball you will use a polished-brass doorknob.

You will connect the can to an uncharged electroscope by means of a wire. You will charge the doorknob by contact with one of the electrified materials suggested on the following pages so that it will acquire a negative charge.

On lowering the charged doorknob into the can without touching the inside of the can, the leaves of the electroscope will diverge. The free electrons on the can's inside surface will be repelled to the outer surface and to the electroscope (see page 62). On withdrawing the doorknob without touching the sides of the can, the leaves will fall. Try lowering and then removing the doorknob several times. Do the electrons return to the inner surface after the doorknob is removed? Explain.

You will now lower the charged doorknob again but

this time let it touch the sides or bottom of the can. The leaves will stay in the same position as before you allowed the doorknob to make contact. Now remove the doorknob from the can. The electroscope will show no change whatsoever; the leaves stay fixed, that is, as diverged as before.

When the doorknob is tested, no charge will be found remaining on it. The inside of the can, tested with a pith ball, will also show no charge.

What takes place? When the doorknob touches the inside of the can, negative charges leave the doorknob and neutralize an equal number of positive charges on the inner surface of the can. The fact that the leaves of the electroscope remain in exactly the same position after the doorknob makes contact shows that no extra negative charges moved to the outer surface of the can. This proves that the number of *induced* positive charges is equal to the number of negative charges on the doorknob. Exactly the same results are obtained even when the most sensitive electroscope is employed in the experiment.

Faraday's experiment, though relatively simple, was of profound importance in the history of electricity. It enabled him to prove experimentally what had, until then, been deduced from theoretical considerations: The total induced charge due to any charged body is always equal to the inducing charge.

WHAT TO DO

...prove that a charged body always induces equal and opposite charges on conductors that surround it.

1. Prepare the simple materials for the "ice-pail" experiment.

DO THIS

Tape bare wire to bottom of can. If possible use flexible aluminum wire of about .035″ gage.

coffee can on paraffin block insulator

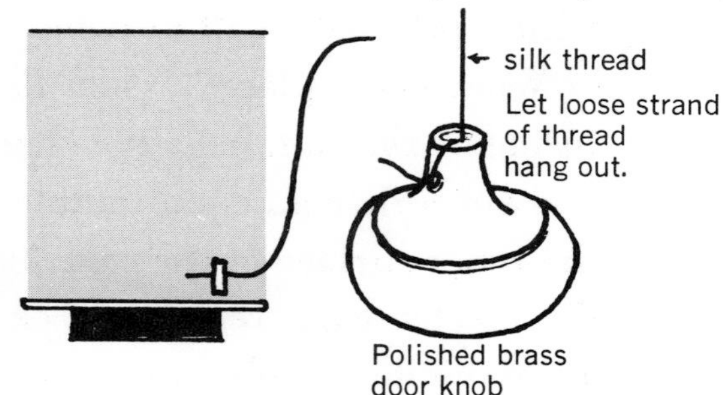

2. Effect of lowering a charged body into can.

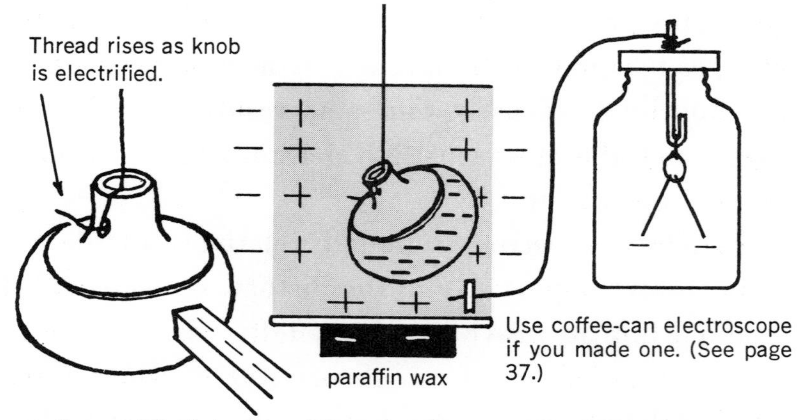

a. Suspend knob by thread. Charge knob by contact with electrified sealing wax or hard-rubber comb or plastic ruler. Rub on wool or fur. Then rub electrified object over knob. Repeat several times.

b. **Without** touching sides or bottom, lower the charged doorknob into can. Observe the electroscope. Now remove charged knob **without** touching can. Do leaves fall when knob is removed from can? Try this several times. Explain.

3. Effect of letting charged body touch the inside of the can.

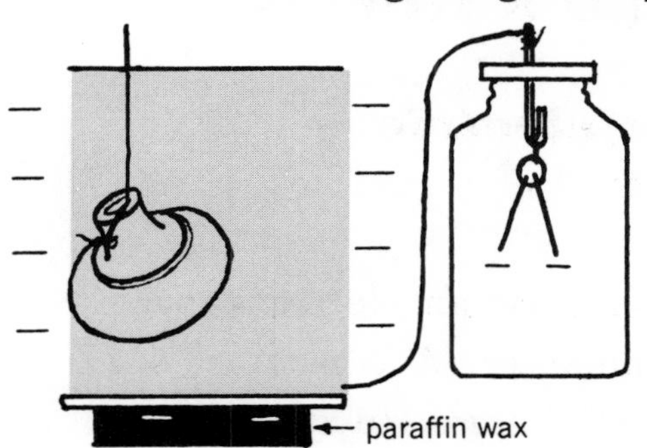

Let charged knob touch sides and bottom of can. Notice that the leaves remain as diverged as before. Remove the knob. The leaves remain diverged. Why?

4. Checking charges after removing knob.

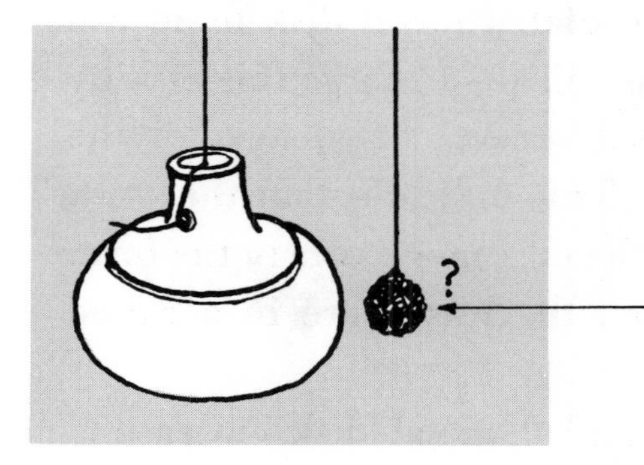

a. Now bring the knob near a suspended pith ball — or a bit of cork at the end of a silk thread. Any attraction? Is there any charge left on the knob? Explain.

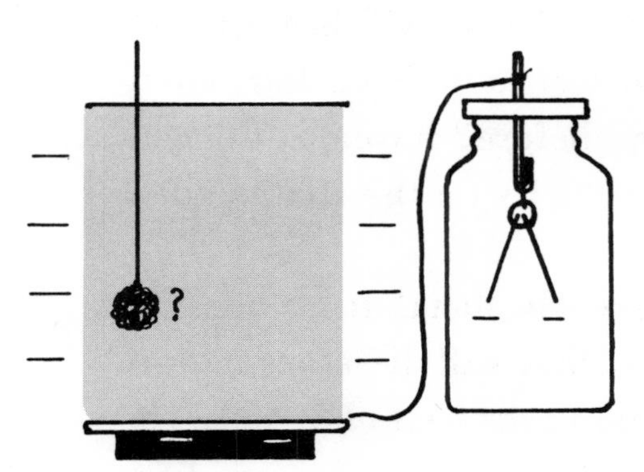

b. Now touch the inside of the can with your pith-ball detector. Any charge on inside? Explain.

c. Try the outside of the can. Any charge there? Explain.

WHAT YOU SHOULD KNOW

. . . about the electric capacitor

You are going to make and use an electric capacitor, sometimes called a condenser. A *capacitor* is a device that stores up electric charges. In its simplest form a capacitor consists of two parallel conducting plates separated by an insulator. The insulator may be air, mica, glass, paper, or some other dielectric.

You will connect an insulated metal disk to an uncharged electroscope. You will then charge this disk by contact with an electrified object. The leaves of the electroscope will diverge. This indicates that the work you invested in charging the disk now exists in the form of potential energy — i.e., the leaves are in a raised position.

You will bring a grounded metal disk closer and closer to the charged disk. The leaves will begin to fall together. Does the charged disk now have *less* potential energy (potential) than before? Explain. Remember that the quantity of electricity on the charged disk remains the same.

Let us assume that you gave the metal disk a negative charge. The nearby grounded disk will therefore acquire a positive charge by induction (see pages 62, 63). The opposite charges on the facing surfaces of the two disks are thus drawn or *bound* to each other. Some negative charges will move from the leaves towards the disk, causing the former to fall. Why?

It is possible to restore the original divergence of the leaves by conveying additional charges to the insulated disk. Try it. In other words the capacity of the insulated disk for storing electricity has been increased by the presence nearby of another disk connected to the earth. The ability of a capacitor to store electricity is called *capacitance*. Three factors influence capacitance: the area of the plates, the distance between the plates, and the nature of the insulating material.

The unit of capacitance is called the *farad* in honor of Michael Faraday. For practical purposes smaller units are used. A microfarad, μf, is a millionth of a farad; a micromicrofarad, $\mu\mu$f, is a millionth of a microfarad. The variable air capacitors used in radio circuits have a capacity of the order of 10 to 400 $\mu\mu$f.

After your capacitor is charged, you will connect the two disks by means of a wire conductor. The negative charges will flow through the wire and neutralize the positive charges. The capacitor has thus been discharged. Explain the effect on the electroscope.

WHAT TO DO

. . . using a homemade capacitor to store electric charges

1. Make these parts for your simple capacitor.

DO THIS

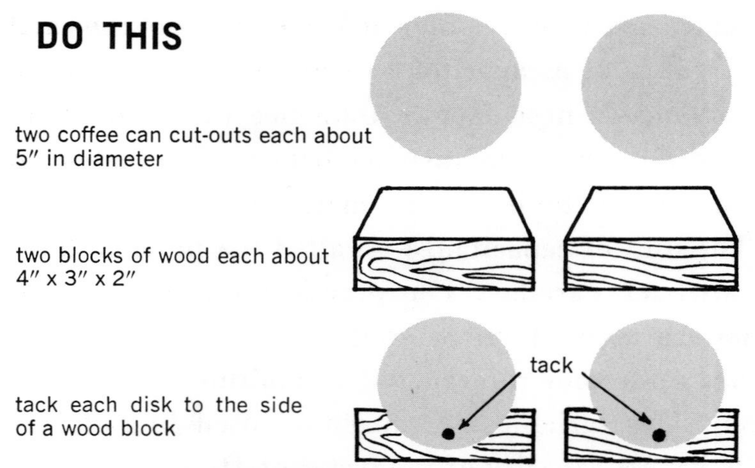

2. Charge the **insulated** metal conductor.

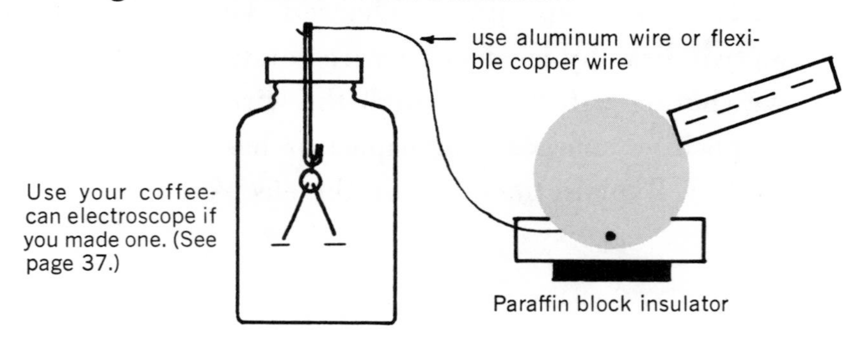

a. Connect stem of electroscope to metal disk by forcing end of wire between disc and wood block.

b. Electrify sealing wax or hard-rubber comb or plastic ruler (fur or wool). Touch electrified object to disk. Rub object again and repeat. Do this until leaves of electroscope diverge sharply.

3. How to increase the capacity of your insulated metal disk for holding electric charges.

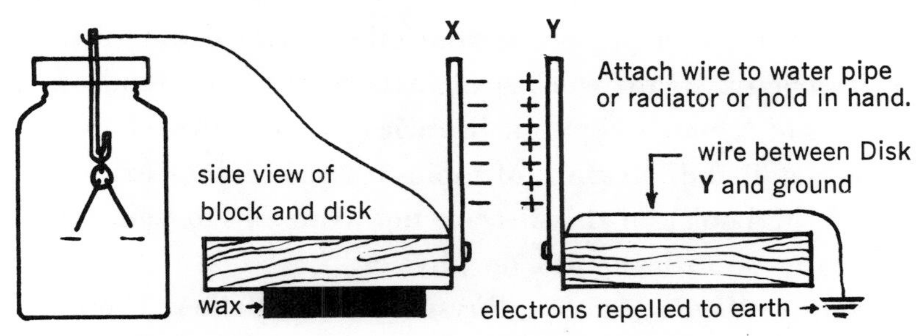

a. Disk **X** resting on insulator was charged in part 2. Now bring Disk **Y** closer and closer to Disk **X**. Do the leaves of electroscope fall slightly? Explain.

b. Now bring the two disks parallel and as close together as possible **without** making contact. Do the leaves fall still more? Why?

4. Add charges to Disk **X** until leaves return to their original divergence.

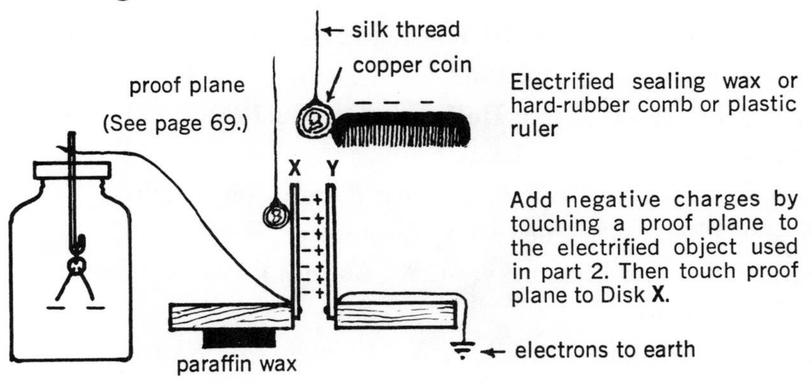

Apply charged proof plane to Disk **X** several times. Electrify the charged body (see above) each time. How many applications of the proof plane, that is, of additional small charges, will make the leaves diverge to original positions? Explain.

5. Place a piece of waxed paper between the disks. Now bring each disk close enough to press against the waxed paper. Explain the effect on the leaves of the electroscope.

FURTHER READING

Most textbooks in physics devote one or two chapters to static electricity. Below is a list of texts commonly found on the shelves of school and public libraries. Consult these books for more-detailed discussions of topics treated in your experiments. If the books on this list are not available to you, try any recently published work on physics.

Asimov, Isaac, *Understanding Physics*, vol. 2. Walker, 1966.

Dull, C. E., Metcalfe, H. C., Williams, J. E., *Modern Physics*, Holt, Rhinehart and Winston, 1964.

Efron, Alexander, *Basic Physics*. Rider, 1957.

Gamow, G., and Cleveland, J. M., *Physics—Foundations and Frontiers*. Prentice-Hall, 1964.

Graham, Kennard C., *Fundamentals of Electricity*. Amer. Tech. Soc., 1961.

MacLachlan, J. H., McNeill, K. G., and Bell, J. M., *Matter and Energy*. Clarke, Irwin, 1963.

Marburger, W. G., and Hoffman, C. W., *Physics for Our Times*. McGraw-Hill, 1958.

Marcus, Abraham, *Basic Electricity*. Prentice-Hall, 1964.

Physics, Physical Science Study Committee, Heath, 1965.

Sears, F. W., and Zemansky, M. W., *College Physics*. Addison-Wesley, 1961.

Smith, A. W., and Cooper, J. N., *Elements of Physics*. McGraw-Hill, 1964.

Taylor, Lloyd W., *Physics, the Pioneer Science*, vol. 2. Dover, 1959 edition (paperback). Interesting presentation of the historical backgrounds of important discoveries in static electricity.

Upton, Monroe, *Electronics for Everyone*, 3rd ed. Devin-Adair, 1963.

Verwiebe, F. L., Van Hooft, G. E., and Suchy, R. R., *Physics — A Basic Science.* Van Nostrand, 1962.

White, Harvey, *Modern College Physics,* 5th ed., Van Nostrand, 1966.

Please note that various aspects of static electricity are often thoroughly explained in encyclopedias. It always helps to spend a little time consulting the index volume. You might try these:

Encyclopaedia Britannica, 1967.

Collier's Encyclopedia, 1966.

Encyclopedia Americana, 1965.

McGraw-Hill Encyclopedia of Science, 1960.

Van Nostrand's Scientific Encyclopedia, 1958.

GLOSSARY

CAPACITOR — a device for the storage of electric charge; it consists essentially of two conducting plates separated by an insulator, called a dielectric.

CONDUCTOR — any material capable of transmitting electricity; silver, copper, and aluminum, for example, contain loosely held electrons that can move readily from point to point.

DIELECTRIC — the term applied to the insulating material that separates the plates of an electric capacitor.

ELECTRIC CHARGE — the result of a disturbance in the balance between electrons and protons in a material; a body that has either an excess or deficiency of electrons is said to be charged.

ELECTRIFICATION — the process of charging a body with electricity.

ELECTRIC FIELD — the region in which an electric force acts on a charge brought into the region.

ELECTRON — a small, mobile, indivisible unit of negative electric charge; one of the constituents of every atom.

ELECTROSTATIC INDUCTION — the general term for the redistribution of electrons on a conductor due to changes in the charges of neighboring bodies.

ELECTROSTATICS — the science which deals with electricity at rest. More exactly, it is *also* concerned with electricity *in motion;* for example, the motion of negative electric charges is involved in electric induction of conductors and in the charging and discharging of a capacitor.

ELECTROSTATIC SHIELDING — a region enclosed by a conductor will not be influenced by any electrostatic fields outside the enclosure.

FARAD — the unit of electrical capacitance used to express the electrical size of a capacitor.

INSULATOR — in electricity, any material that does not conduct an electric current.

ION — an atom or molecule that has gained or lost one or more electrons and thus become a carrier of electric charge; in a gas some of the negative ions may be free electrons.

IONIZATION — the process by which ions are formed; in gases, ions are usually produced by the forcible collision of gas atoms with other particles.

NEGATIVE CHARGE — the kind of charge produced on hard rubber when stroked with fur; the result of a surplus of electrons on a body.

POSITIVE CHARGE — the kind of charge produced on glass when stroked with silk; the result of a deficit of electrons on a body.

PROTON — one of the fundamental particles located in the nuclei of atoms; each proton has a positive charge equal in amount to that of the negatively charged electron.

INDEX

The Author

HARRY SOOTIN has taught general science and physics in the New York City high schools for more than twenty-five years. A graduate of the City College of New York, Mr. Sootin began his career as a chemist and soon switched to teaching. He was a member of the faculty of the High School of Commerce in Manhattan and then taught at Flushing High School on Long Island. He has always favored the laboratory approach to science teaching, believing that it is most effective in interesting his students in scientific facts and ideas.

In addition to his teaching duties, Mr. Sootin has devoted much of his time to writing. He is the author of some eleven books for young people, including biographies of Isaac Newton, Michael Faraday, Gregor Mendel, and Robert Boyle. Mr. Sootin has written many science articles for magazines and for the *Book of Knowledge*. He is a member of the American Association for the Advancement of Science, the History of Science Society, and the Teachers' Guild.